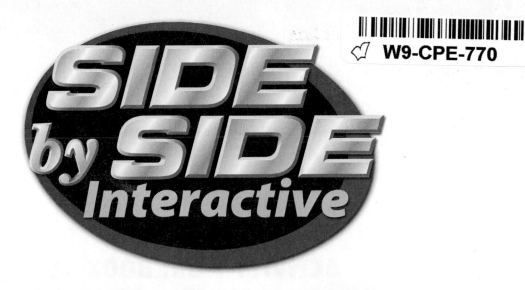

SIDE by SIDE Interactive

ACTIVITY WORKBOOK

1B

A self-study companion to
Side by Side Interactive **multimedia software**
and
Side by Side TV **videos**

Steven J. Molinsky

Bill Bliss

Contributing Authors
Elizabeth Handley
Judy Boyle

Longman

longman.com

ACTIVITY WORKBOOK 1B

Side by Side Interactive Activity Workbook 1B
Copyright © 2004 by Prentice Hall Regents
Addison Wesley Longman, Inc.
A Pearson Education Company.

Pearson Education, 10 Bank Street, White Plains, NY 10606

Editorial manager: *Pam Fishman*
Vice president, director of design and production: *Rhea Banker*
Director of electronic production: *Aliza Greenblatt*
Production manager: *Ray Keating*
Director of manufacturing: *Patrice Fraccio*
Associate digital layout manager: *Paula D. Williams*
Cover design: *Monika Popowitz*

Project manager: *Harriet Dishman*
Design and composition: *PC&F, Inc.*
Video stills: *Elizabeth Gallagher*
Illustrator: *Richard E. Hill*

The authors gratefully acknowledge the contribution
of Tina Carver in the development of the original
Side by Side program.

ISBN 0-13-110762-3

1 2 3 4 5 6 7 8 9 10 – WC – 06 05 04 03

CONTENTS

• • • • • PREFACE • • • • •

The **Side by Side Interactive** Activity Workbooks are designed to serve as self-study companions to the **Side by Side Interactive** multimedia software program and the **Side by Side TV** videos. The Activity Workbooks supplement the technology-based language instruction through motivating activities that are individualized, self-paced, easy-to-use, and fun!

This volume, Activity Workbook 1B, provides up to 60 hours of supplemental practice for Level 1B (Segments 14-26) of the program. It can be used at home, in school, or in any other setting. (The total program contains 52 segments. Learners who complete one segment each week can therefore complete the program in one year.)

FEATURES OF THE ACTIVITY WORKBOOK

- SEGMENT OPENING PAGES indicate the language focus and key vocabulary in the segment and describe the scenes, songs, and other video-based lessons contained in the multimedia software program and in the videos.

- EXERCISES and ACTIVITIES help learners interact with the video-based lessons in each segment. Certain exercises and activities require use of the video material and are indicated with the symbol 🔑. Learners can choose to do these exercises and activities before, during, or after they watch the video material.

- SCRIPTS are provided at the end of each workbook segment. Learners can read along as they watch, read before to preview the material, or read later for review and practice.

- A SUMMARY PAGE provides grammar charts and highlights functional expressions featured in each segment.

- An ANSWER KEY enables learners to check their work.

The mission of *Side by Side Interactive* and *Side by Side TV* is to offer learners of English exciting, motivating, and effective language instruction through multimedia software and video. We hope that this companion Activity Workbook helps to provide a language-learning experience that is dynamic, interactive, . . . and fun!

Steven J. Molinsky
Bill Bliss

HOW TO READ LESSON HEADINGS:

Side by Side Interactive
Segment & Lesson Number

↓

1.1 WHAT'S YOUR NAME?　(:09) ◄—　*Side by Side TV*
Video Clock Time

↑
Lesson Title

To find the video material for lessons in this workbook:
Side by Side Interactive multimedia software users should use the Segment & Lesson Numbers.
Side by Side TV video users should use the Video Clock Times.

🔑 indicates a workbook activity that requires the user to view the corresponding video material—either in the multimedia software program or in the videos.

SEGMENT 14

- Simple Present Tense
- Yes/No Questions
- Negatives
- Short Answers

"For a very special dinner Stanley's Restaurant is a winner . . . eating Side by Side."

LESSON MENU

14.1 STANLEY'S INTERNATIONAL RESTAURANT (:09)
Stanley's Restaurant is a very special place. Every day Stanley cooks a different kind of food.

14.2 WE'RE FILMING A COMMERCIAL (2:07)
An interviewer talks to passersby about Stanley's International Restaurant.

14.3 A VERY SPECIAL PLACE (3:55)
An interview with Stanley the chef.

SBS-TV Backstage Bulletin Board

TO: Production Crew
Sets and props for this segment:

Stanley's Kitchen
pots
pans
tablecloth

Reception Desk
telephone
flags

Inside Stanley's Restaurant
tables
dishes
tablecloths
chairs
silverware

Outside Stanley's Restaurant
microphone

TO: Cast Members
Key words in this segment:

American
Chinese
Greek
Italian
Japanese
Mexican
Puerto Rican

Monday
Tuesday
Wednesday
Thursday
Friday
Saturday
Sunday

14.1 STANLEY'S INTERNATIONAL RESTAURANT (:09)

SOUND CHECK 1

Monday

1 (a.) Italian
   b. Thai

Tuesday

2 a. Korean
   b. Greek

Wednesday

3 a. Chinese
   b. Japanese

Thursday

4 a. Puerto Rican
   b. Portuguese

Friday

5 a. Japanese
   b. Taiwanese

Saturday

6 a. Moroccan
   b. Mexican

Sunday

7 a. American
   b. Middle Eastern

SOUND CHECK 2

| cook | cooks | does |

A. Stanley's International Restaurant.

B. What kind of food does Stanley _____cook_____[1] on Monday?

A. On Monday he _____[2] Italian food.

B. Thank you.

A. Stanley's International Restaurant.

B. What kind of food _____[3]
Stanley _____[4] on Wednesday?

A. On Wednesday he _____[5]
Chinese food.

B. Chinese food?

A. Yes, that's right.

B. Thank you.

A. Stanley's International Restaurant.

B. _____[6] Stanley _____[7]
Greek food on Tuesday?

A. Yes, he _____[8].

B. Thank you.

A. Stanley's Restaurant.

B. Does Stanley _____[9] Puerto
Rican food on Thursday?

A. Yes, he _____[10].

B. Thanks.

ON CAMERA

You work at Stanley's Restaurant. Complete the following conversations.

A. Good morning. Stanley's Restaurant.

B. Good morning. What kind of food does
Stanley cook on ....?

A. On .... he cooks
.... food.

B. Thank you.

A. Good evening. Stanley's Restaurant.

B. Does Stanley cook ....
food on ....?

A. Yes, he does.

B. Thanks.

doesn't   does   cook   cooks

A. _____Does_____ [1] Stanley cook Japanese food on Sunday?

B. No, he _____ [2].

A. When _____ [3] he _____ [4] Japanese food?

B. He _____ [5] Japanese food on Friday.

A. Excuse me?

B. Yes, ma'am.

A. _____ [6] Stanley _____ [7] Chinese food on Monday?

B. No, he _____ [8].

A. When _____ [9] he _____ [10] Chinese food?

B. He _____ [11] Chinese food on Wednesday.

A. I see. Thank you.

ON CAMERA

You're the manager at Stanley's International Restaurant. People are asking you questions about Stanley's menu. Complete these conversations and then practice them with a friend.

A. Excuse me.

B. Yes?

A. Does Stanley cook ....

   food on ....?

B. Yes, he does.

A. Oh, great! I like ....

   food! See you on ....!

A. Does Stanley cook ....

   food on ....?

B. No, he doesn't.

A. I see. Tell me, when does he cook

   .... food?

B. He cooks .... food

   on ....

A. Oh. Thanks very much.

14.2 WE'RE FILMING A COMMERCIAL (2:07)

SOUND CHECK

cook	go	doesn't	like	do	don't

A. _____ Do _____ ¹ you _____² to Stanley's Restaurant on Wednesday?

B. Yes, I _____³.

A. Why?

B. Because I _____⁴ Chinese food.

A. Thank you very much, sir.

B. My pleasure.

A. _____⁵ you _____⁶ to Stanley's Restaurant on Sunday?

B. No, I _____⁷.

A. Why not?

B. Because I _____ _____⁸ American food.

A. I see. Well, thank you anyway.

A. What kind of food _____⁹ you _____¹⁰?

B. I _____¹¹ Russian food.

A. When _____¹² you _____¹³ to Stanley's Restaurant?

B. I _____¹⁴ go there.

A. Why not?

B. Because Stanley _____ _____¹⁵ Russian food.

You're filming a commercial for Stanley's Restaurant. Complete these interviews and then practice them.

Daily Specials

Italian   Greek   ~~Chinese~~   Puerto Rican   Japanese   Mexican   American

Commercial #1
Location: Outside Stanley's Restaurant

YOU: Excuse me. We're filming a commercial for Stanley's Restaurant. May I ask you a few questions?

PERSON ON STREET: Of course.

YOU: Do you go to Stanley's Restaurant on ....?

PERSON ON STREET: Yes, I do.

YOU: Why?

PERSON ON STREET: Because I like .... food.

YOU: Thank you.

PERSON ON STREET: My pleasure.

Commercial #2
Location: Inside Stanley's Restaurant

YOU: Excuse me.
We're filming a commercial.
May I ask you a few questions?

PERSON IN RESTAURANT: Certainly.

YOU: Do you go to Stanley's Restaurant on ....?

PERSON IN RESTAURANT: No, I don't.

YOU: You don't? Why not?

PERSON IN RESTAURANT: Because on .... he cooks ....

food, and I don't like .... food.

YOU: I see. Thank you anyway.

Commercial #3
Location: Outside Stanley's Restaurant

YOU: Excuse me. We're filming a television commercial. May I ask you a few questions?

PERSON ON STREET: Sure.

YOU: Tell me, what kind of food do you like?

PERSON ON STREET: I like .... food.

YOU: .... food?

PERSON ON STREET: Yes, that's right.

YOU: When do you go to Stanley's Restaurant?

PERSON ON STREET: I don't go there.

YOU: Why not?

PERSON ON STREET: Because Stanley doesn't cook

.... food.

YOU: He doesn't?

PERSON ON STREET: No, he doesn't.

SCRAMBLED SOUND TRACK

The sound track is all mixed up. Put the words in the correct order.

1 | to | on | Do | Restaurant | Tuesday | you | Stanley's | ? | go |

Do you go to Stanley's Restaurant on Tuesday?

2 | you | kind | What | do | of | ? | like | food |

_____

3 | French | doesn't | . | Stanley | cook | food |

_____

4 | Friday | ? | cook | Does | food | on | Chinese | Stanley |

_____

5 | because | Sunday | Restaurant | I | American | to | like | go | food | . | on | don't |

| Stanley's | I | don't |

_____

14.3 A VERY SPECIAL PLACE (3:55)

The video editor made a mistake! Put the following lines in the correct order.

_____ Thank you.

_____ speak Greek,

_____ speak Italian,

_____ eat Greek food,

_____ drink Italian wine,

_____ and listen to Greek music.

_____ On Monday they

_____ drink Greek wine,

_____ On Tuesday they

_____ and listen to Italian music.

_____ What do people do at Stanley's International Restaurant?

_____ eat Italian food,

___1___ Stanley, your restaurant is a very special place.

STANLEY'S FAVORITE CUSTOMERS

1 Maria likes Chinese food. When does she go to Stanley's Restaurant?

_____

What does she do there?

_____

_____

2 George likes Mexican food. When does he go to Stanley's Restaurant?

_____

What does he do there?

_____

_____

3 Mr. and Mrs. Wong like Greek food. When do they go to Stanley's Restaurant?

_____

What do they do there?

_____

_____

WHAT'S MY LINE?

1. (like)   I _____like_____ American food. My wife _____ Greek food.

2. (work)   Barbara _____ at the bank. Her brother _____ at the post office.

3. (listen)   We _____ to the radio in our car. Do you _____ to the radio in your car?

4. (study)   I _____ French, and my sister _____ German.

5. (go)   We _____ to Stanley's Restaurant on Tuesday. Our next-door neighbor _____ there on Friday.

6. (speak)   The students in this class _____ many different languages. Kenji _____ Japanese. Kim _____ Korean. Manuel and Elena _____ Spanish.

7. (cook)   Mr. Lane _____ dinner on Monday. Mrs. Lane _____ dinner on Wednesday. Their son _____ dinner on Friday.

DO THEY OR DON'T THEY?

do	does	don't	doesn't

1. Do you exercise every day?   Yes, I _____do_____.

2. Does your daughter study every night?   Yes, she _____.

3. Does Mr. Chang work here?   No, he _____.

4. Do your children like their new school? Yes, they _____.

5. Does your boss speak Spanish?   Yes, he _____.

6. Do you like American food?   No, we _____.

7. Do Mr. and Mrs. Ford live nearby?   No, they _____.

8. Do I ask a lot of questions?   Yes, you _____.

9. Does Betty play the guitar?   No, she _____.

10. Do you work on Saturday?   No, I _____.

14.1 STANLEY'S INTERNATIONAL RESTAURANT (:09)

ANNOUNCER: Stanley's International Restaurant is a very special place. Every day Stanley cooks a different kind of food. On Monday he cooks Italian food. On Tuesday he cooks Greek food. On Wednesday he cooks Chinese food. On Thursday he cooks Puerto Rican food. On Friday he cooks Japanese food. On Saturday he cooks Mexican food. And on Sunday he cooks American food.

(The cashier answers the phone.)

CASHIER: Stanley's International Restaurant.
CALLER 1: What kind of food does Stanley cook on Monday?
CASHIER: On Monday he cooks Italian food.
CALLER 1: Thank you.

CASHIER: Stanley's International Restaurant.
CALLER 2: What kind of food does Stanley cook on Wednesday?
CASHIER: On Wednesday he cooks Chinese food.
CALLER 2: Chinese food?
CASHIER: Yes, that's right.
CALLER 2: Thank you.

CASHIER: Stanley's International Restaurant.
CALLER 3: Does Stanley cook Greek food on Tuesday?
CASHIER: Yes, he does.
CALLER 3: Thank you.

CASHIER: Stanley's Restaurant.
CALLER 4: Does Stanley cook Puerto Rican food on Thursday?
CASHIER: Yes, he does.
CALLER 4: Thanks.

CUSTOMER 1: Does Stanley cook Japanese food on Sunday?
WAITER: No, he doesn't.
CUSTOMER 1: When does he cook Japanese food?
WAITER: He cooks Japanese food on Friday.

CUSTOMER 2: Excuse me?
WAITER: Yes, ma'am.
CUSTOMER 2: I have a question. Does Stanley cook Chinese food on Monday?
WAITER: No, he doesn't.
CUSTOMER 2: When does he cook Chinese food?
WAITER: He cooks Chinese food on Wednesday.
CUSTOMER 2: I see. Thank you.

14.2 WE'RE FILMING A COMMERCIAL (2:07)

INTERVIEWER: Excuse me, sir. We're filming a commercial for Stanley's

Restaurant. May I ask you one or two questions?

MAN 1: Certainly. Go right ahead.

CAMERAMAN: Rolling!

INTERVIEWER: Do you go to Stanley's Restaurant on Wednesday?

MAN 1: Yes, I do.

INTERVIEWER: Why?

MAN 1: Because I like Chinese food.

INTERVIEWER: Thank you very much, sir.

MAN 1: My pleasure.

INTERVIEWER: Excuse me. We're filming a commercial.

WOMAN: A commercial? You mean . . . a TV commercial?!

INTERVIEWER: Yes. May I ask you one or two questions?

WOMAN: Sure.

CAMERAMAN: Rolling!

INTERVIEWER: Do you go to Stanley's Restaurant on Sunday?

WOMAN: No, I don't.

INTERVIEWER: Why not?

WOMAN: Because I don't like American food.

INTERVIEWER: I see. Well, thank you anyway.

INTERVIEWER: Excuse me, sir. We're doing a commercial. May I ask you a few questions?

MAN 2: Sure.

INTERVIEWER: What kind of food do you like?

MAN 2: I like Russian food.

INTERVIEWER: When do you go to Stanley's Restaurant?

MAN 2: I don't go there.

INTERVIEWER: Why not?

MAN 2: Because Stanley doesn't cook Russian food.

INTERVIEWER: Cut!

(To the cameraman.)

Stanley doesn't cook Russian food?

CAMERAMAN: No, he doesn't.

MAN 2: No, he doesn't.

INTERVIEWER: Thanks anyway.

MAN 2: No problem.

(To the cameraman.)

INTERVIEWER: Why didn't you tell me he doesn't cook Russian food?

14.3   A VERY SPECIAL PLACE   (3:55)

INTERVIEWER: Stanley, your restaurant is a very special place.

STANLEY: Thank you.

INTERVIEWER: What do people do at Stanley's International Restaurant?

STANLEY: On Monday, they speak Italian, eat Italian food, drink Italian wine, and listen to Italian music. On Tuesday, they speak Greek, eat Greek food, drink Greek wine, and listen to Greek music. On Wednesday, they speak Chinese, eat Chinese food, drink Chinese…

INTERVIEWER: Thank you, Stanley. Yes, Stanley's International Restaurant is a very special place. So come on over to Stanley's Restaurant, the International Restaurant, where Stanley cooks a different kind of food every day. Okay?

CAMERAMAN: It's a wrap.

STANLEY: It's a wrap?!

INTERVIEWER: Yes. We're finished.

STANLEY: It's a wrap!

GRAMMAR

Simple Present Tense: Yes/No Questions

Do	I we you they	go to Stanley's Restaurant?
Does	he she it	

Negatives

I We You They	don't	like American food.
He She It	doesn't	

Short Answers

Yes,	I we you they	do.
	he she it	does.

No,	I we you they	don't.
	he she it	doesn't.

FUNCTIONS

Asking for and Reporting Information

What *do you do there?*
What kind of *food does Stanley cook on Monday?*
When *does he cook Japanese food?*

Do you *go to Stanley's Restaurant?*
   Yes, I do.
   No, I don't.

Does *Stanley cook Greek food on Tuesday?*
   Yes, he does.
   No, he doesn't.

May I ask you *a few questions?*

Inquiring about Likes/Dislikes

What kind of *food* do you like?

Expressing Likes

I like *Chinese food.*

Expressing Dislikes

I don't like *American food.*

Checking Understanding

Chinese food?

Attracting Attention

Excuse me.

SEGMENT 15

- **Favorite Types of Entertainment**
- **Simple Present Tense**

"Our favorite sport, our favorite book, our favorite food

we like to cook . . . together Side by Side."

LESSON MENU

15.1 **SBS-TV ON LOCATION** (5:04)
People tell their favorite movies, books, music, and sports.

15.2 **FAMILY FAVORITES** (7:26)
A husband and wife try to guess each other's favorite kinds of movies, books, music, sports, and TV programs.
Host: Rich Young.

SBS-TV Backstage Bulletin Board

TO: Production Crew
Sets and props for this segment:

TV Studio
   cards   markers   microphone

TO: Cast Members
Key words in this segment:

book	classical music
movie	jazz
music	opera
sport	popular music
TV program	rock music
What kind of . . . ?	baseball
favorite	football
like	golf
adventure movie	hockey
cartoon	soccer
comedy	tennis
drama	actor
science fiction	actress
western	author
novel	poet
poetry	performer
short story	
game show	
news program	

15.1 SBS-TV ON LOCATION (5:04)

Help the actors prepare their lines.

Movies			
a. adventure movie	b. cartoon	c. comedy	d. drama
	e. science fiction movie		f. western

1. _d_   2. ____   3. ____

4. ____   5. ____   6. ____

Books		
a. novel	b. poetry	c. short story

7. ____   8. ____   9. ____

TV Programs				
a. cartoon	b. comedy	c. drama	d. game show	e. news program

10. ____   11. ____   12. ____   13. ____   14. ____

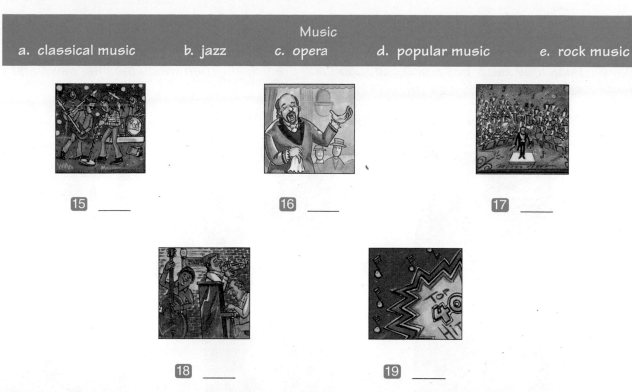

15 ____   16 ____   17 ____

18 ____   19 ____

Sports

a. baseball   b. football   c. golf   d. hockey   e. soccer   f. tennis

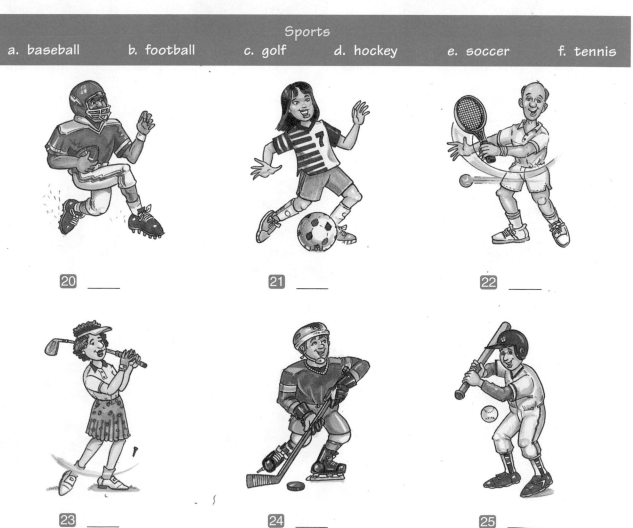

20 ____   21 ____   22 ____

23 ____   24 ____   25 ____

Before you watch the interviews, look at these people. What kind of movies do you think they like? Put a circle around each prediction. Then watch the interviews and see how many of your predictions are correct.

What kind of movies do you like?

1 (a.) comedies

2 a. adventure movies

3 a. science fiction movies

　b. science fiction movies

　b. comedies

　b. dramas

4 a. cartoons

5 a. westerns

6 a. adventure movies

　b. science fiction movies

　b. dramas

　b. cartoons

SOUND CHECK

Who is your favorite actor or actress?

1 (a.) Goldie Hawn

2 a. Garrison Ward

3 a. Marla Street

　b. Gilda Horn

　b. Harrison Ford

　b. Meryl Streep

4 a. Leonard Nimoy

5 a. John Wang

6 a. Mickey Mouse

　b. Bennet Nimoy

　b. John Wayne

　b. Mighty Mouse

You're editing the interviews with these people. Which words does each person say?

What kind of books do you like? Who is your favorite author or poet?

1
- a. novels
- b. poetry
- c. Tom Clancy
- d. Tom Cranston

2
- a. novels
- b. poetry
- c. Emily Nickerson
- d. Emily Dickinson

3
- a. poetry
- b. short stories
- c. Edgar Allan Pope
- d. Edgar Allan Poe

CAN YOU PREDICT?

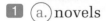

Before you watch the interviews, predict what these people are going to say. Then watch and check your answers.

What kind of TV programs do you like?

1
- a. cartoons
- b. game shows

2
- a. game shows
- b. news programs

3
- a. comedies
- b. news programs

4
- a. comedies
- b. dramas

5
- a. cartoons
- b. comedies

WHAT'S MY LINE?

I like _____.[1]

My wife likes _____.[2]

CAN YOU PREDICT?

Before you watch the interviews, predict what these people are going to say. Then watch and check your answers.

What kind of music do you like?

1. a. classical music
   b. rock music

2. a. jazz
   b. opera music

3. a. popular music
   b. rock music

4. a. classical music
   b. popular music

5. a. jazz
   b. opera music

SOUND CHECK

Who is your favorite performer?

1. a. Bryce Springstone
   b. Bruce Springsteen

2. a. Dave Brubeck
   b. Dave Brubaker

3. a. Margaret Dreisand
   b. Barbra Streisand

4. a. Zack Berlin
   b. Itzhak Perlman

5. a. Pavel Gotty
   b. Pavarotti

CAN YOU PREDICT?

Before you watch the interviews, predict what these people are going to say. Then watch and check your answers.

What's your favorite sport?

1   a. football   **2**   a. football   **3**   a. baseball

      (b.) tennis   b. baseball   b. golf

4   a. baseball   **5**   a. football   **6**   a. hockey

      b. soccer   b. golf   b. tennis

CLOSE-UP

You're on Side by Side TV! Tell about YOUR favorites.

1   What kind of movies do you like?   ....

2   Who is your favorite actor or actress?   ....

3   What kind of books do you like?   ....

4   Who is your favorite author?   ....

5   What kind of TV programs do you like?   ....

6   What kind of music do you like?   ....

7   Who is your favorite performer?   ....

8   What's your favorite sport?   ....

INTERVIEW

Interview a friend. Ask about his or her favorites and write the answers below.

1   Movies: ....   **3**   TV Programs: ....

2   Books: ....   **4**   Music: ....

           5   Sport: ....

15.2 FAMILY FAVORITES (7:26)

GUESTS AND HOST

1. Rich Young is _____.

   a. a contestant

   b. the host

2. Dave and Donna Dawson live in _____.

   a. Denver

   b. Dallas

3. Dave is originally from _____.

   a. Denver

   b. Dallas

4. Donna is originally from _____.

   a. Des Moines

   b. Detroit

EDITING MIX-UP 1

The video editor made a mistake! Put the following lines in the correct order.

_____ I know my wife. She likes comedies.

_____ Comedies!

_____ Congratulations, Dave and Donna.
You're off to a good start. You have $100.

_____ What is Donna's favorite kind of movie?

_____ Okay, Donna and Dave. Time's up!
Dave, what kind of movies does Donna
like?

_____ So Donna, what is your favorite kind of movie?
Dave, what kind of movie is Donna's favorite?
Write your answers down on the cards.

_1_ Do you have your cards and markers ready? I see you do.
Then let's begin. It's time for our first question.

_____ All right. Now let's see. Donna, what kind of movies do you like?

1 a. What kind of books does Dave like?

   b. What kind of books Dave likes?

2 a. So Dave, what kind of books do you like?

   b. So Dave, what kind of books you do like?

3 a. Dave is liking novels.

   b. Dave likes novels.

5 a. Dave, read you novels all the time?

   b. Dave, do you read novels all the time?

4 a. He reads novels all the time.

   b. He reads novels all the time's up.

6 a. Yes, I do.

   b. Yes, I does.

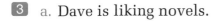

SOUND CHECK 1

do	don't	I	you	like	jazz	kind	what
does	doesn't	she	your	likes	music	of	

RICH YOUNG: And the next question is: What kind of _____music_____ [1] does Donna

_____ [2]? So Donna, what _____ [3] of music do

_____ [4] like? Dave, _____ [5] kind _____ [6]

music does Donna _____ [7]? Okay, Dave and Donna. Time's up!

Let's see _____ [8] answers. Donna, what kind of music

_____ [9] you _____ [10]?

DONNA: I like _____ [11].

RICH YOUNG: Dave, what kind of music _____ [12] Donna _____ [13]?

DAVE: She _____ [14] like jazz. She _____ [15] ROCK music.

DONNA: No, I _____ [16].

DAVE: Yes, you _____ [17].

RICH YOUNG: Dave, _____ [18] doesn't.

DAVE: Yes, she _____ [19].

DONNA: No, _____ [20] don't.

RICH YOUNG: What is Dave's favorite (sport / sports) ¹? Dave, which sport (does / do) ²

(you / your) ³ really (likes / like) ⁴? Donna, (Rich / which) ⁵ sport (does / do) ⁶

Dave (like / likes) ⁷? Okay, Donna, let's see (your / you) ⁸ answer.

What (is / of) ⁹ (Daves / Dave's) ¹⁰ favorite sport?

DONNA: (Baseball / Basketball) ¹¹.

RICH YOUNG: And Dave? (What / What's) ¹² (your / you) ¹³ favorite sport?

DAVE: (Feetball / Football) ¹⁴.

DONNA: Football?! You (don't / doesn't) ¹⁵ (like / likes) ¹⁶ football!

DAVE: Of course I (does / do) ¹⁷! I (LOVES / LOVE) ¹⁸ football!

DONNA: No, you (don't / doesn't) ¹⁹!

DAVE: Yes, I (does / do) ²⁰! I (plays / play) ²¹ football every (day / Saturday) ²²!

The video editor made another mistake! Put the following lines in the correct order.

____ Cartoons. Donna LOVES cartoons!

____ Yes, you do!

____ News programs!

____ No, I don't!

_1_ Dave, what kind of TV programs does Donna like?

____ Cartoons??!! I don't like cartoons!

____ News programs?! Hah! I watch news programs. YOU watch cartoons!

____ Donna, I'm almost afraid to ask. What's your answer?

SCRAMBLED WORDS

There are some problems with the sound track. Fix the scrambled words.

1 Our **aftervoi** sport is hockey.   favorite

2 Do you like **emocides**?

3 He reads **lovens** all the time.

4 Do you play **flog**?

5 My father writes **reptoy.**

6 I definitely like **niecces infotic.**

7 Are you listening to **scalliasc cuism?**

8 We really don't like **duverante viemos.**

9 Beverly Sills is a wonderful **frereprom.**

10 Our children like to watch **norcoast.**

11 I'm writing a **thors styro.**

ON CAMERA

You and a friend are on TV with Rich Young! Using the following as a guide, play "Student Favorites."

RICH YOUNG:	What kind of (movies/books/sports/music/TV programs) does
	.... like?
	(student's name)
STUDENT A:	He/She likes ....
RICH YOUNG:	...., what kind of (movies/books/sports/
	(student's name)
	music/TV programs) do you like?
STUDENT B:	I like ....
RICH YOUNG:	(Congratulations!/I'm very sorry!) You now have .... dollars. Are you ready for the next question?
STUDENT A:	We're ready, Rich.
STUDENT B:	Yes, we're ready.

SENTENCE CHALLENGE!

How many sentences can you make with the words below?

and	Donna	Dave	do	does	doesn't
don't	dramas	like	likes	but	. ?

1 ....
2 ....
3 ....
4 ....
5 ....
6 ....
7 ....
8 ....
9 ....
10 ....

11 ....
12 ....
13 ....
14 ....
15 ....
16 ....
17 ....
18 ....
19 ....
20 ....

AMERICAN CULTURE QUIZ

Do you know the names of American actors and actresses, musical performers, authors, and poets? Write the names below and compare your answers with your friends'.

Actor/Actress	Musical Performer	Author	Poet
....	....	....	....
....	....	....	....
....	....	....	....

SEGMENT 15 SCRIPT ●●●●●●●●●●●●●●●●●●●●●●●●●●●●●●●●●●●●

15.1 SBS-TV ON LOCATION (5:04)

INTERVIEWER:	Do you go to the movies?
PERSON 1:	Yes, I do.
INTERVIEWER:	What kind of movies do you like?
PERSON 1:	I like comedies.
INTERVIEWER:	What kind of movies do you like?
PERSON 2:	I like adventure movies.
PERSON 3:	I like dramas.
PERSON 4:	Hmm. I like science fiction movies.
PERSON 5:	Westerns.
PERSON 6:	I like cartoons.
INTERVIEWER:	Who is your favorite actor or actress?
PERSON 1:	Goldie Hawn. She's funny.
INTERVIEWER:	Who is your favorite actor or actress?
PERSON 2:	It's Harrison Ford. Definitely Harrison Ford.
PERSON 3:	Meryl Streep.
PERSON 4:	My favorite actor is Leonard Nimoy.
PERSON 5:	John Wayne. I still like John Wayne. He's my favorite.
PERSON 6:	You mean my favorite cartoon character? It's Mickey Mouse. Of course!
INTERVIEWER:	Do you read a lot?
PERSON 7:	Yes, I do.
INTERVIEWER:	What kind of books do you like?
PERSON 7:	I like novels.
INTERVIEWER:	Who's your favorite author?
PERSON 7:	Tom Clancy.

INTERVIEWER:	What kind of books do you like?
PERSON 8:	I like poetry.
INTERVIEWER:	Poetry? That's nice. Who's your favorite poet?
PERSON 8:	Emily Dickinson.
PERSON 9:	I like short stories.
INTERVIEWER:	Who's your favorite author?
PERSON 9:	Edgar Allan Poe.
INTERVIEWER:	Do you watch TV a lot?
PERSON 10:	Yes, I do.
INTERVIEWER:	What kind of TV programs do you like?
PERSON 10:	I like game shows.
INTERVIEWER:	What kind of TV programs do you like?
PERSON 11:	I like news programs.
PERSON 1:	I like comedies.
PERSON 5:	Dramas.
PERSON 6:	Cartoons. I like cartoons.
INTERVIEWER:	What kind of music do you like?
PERSON 12:	I like rock music.
INTERVIEWER:	What kind of music do you like?
PERSON 7:	I like jazz.
PERSON 13:	I like popular music.
PERSON 8:	Classical music.
PERSON 11:	I like opera music.
INTERVIEWER:	Who is your favorite performer?
PERSON 12:	Bruce Springsteen.
PERSON 7:	I like Dave Brubeck. He's great.
PERSON 13:	My favorite performer? Let me see. I guess it's Barbra Streisand.
PERSON 8:	Itzhak Perlman.
PERSON 11:	Pavarotti is my favorite. He's terrific.
INTERVIEWER:	Do you like sports?
PERSON 14:	Yes, I do.
INTERVIEWER:	What's your favorite sport?

PERSON 14: Tennis.

INTERVIEWER: What's your favorite sport?

PERSON 6: I like football.

PERSON 5: I like baseball.

PERSON 2: Soccer.

PERSON 7: My favorite sport? Hmm. It's golf.

PERSON 15: I love hockey. Hockey is definitely my favorite sport.

15.2 FAMILY FAVORITES (7:26)

ANNOUNCER: And now it's time to play the world's favorite game show, *Family Favorites*. And here's the world's favorite game show host: Rich Young.

RICH YOUNG: Thank you, ladies and gentlemen. Thank you. Thank you. And welcome to another edition of *Family Favorites*, the game show where husbands and wives find out how much they really know about each other. Let's meet our two contestants. Let's say "Hello" to Dave and Donna Dawson!

Welcome, Dave and Donna. Tell us, Dave, where do you and Donna live?

DAVE: We live in Denver.

RICH YOUNG: Are you originally from Denver?

DAVE: No, we aren't. I'm originally from Dallas, and Donna's originally from Des Moines.

DONNA: No, Dave, that's not right. I'm not from Des Moines. I'm from Detroit.

DAVE: Oh, that's right.

RICH YOUNG: Well, wherever you're from, we're glad you're both here today to play *Family Favorites!* Now, here's how we play our game. I'll ask you both a question about something one of you likes. You'll both write your answers down on the cards in front of you, and we'll see if your answers match. For every match, we'll give you one hundred dollars. Now, are you ready to play our game?

DONNA: Ready, Rich.

DAVE: Yes. I'm ready.

RICH YOUNG: Do you have your cards and markers ready? I see you do. Then let's begin. It's time for our first question. What is Donna's favorite kind of movie? So Donna, what is your favorite kind of movie? Dave, what kind of movie is Donna's favorite? Write your answers down on the cards. Okay, Donna and Dave. Time's up! Dave, what kind of movies does Donna like?

DAVE: I know my wife. She likes comedies.

RICH YOUNG: All right. Now let's see. Donna, what kind of movies do you like?

DONNA: Comedies!

RICH YOUNG: Congratulations, Dave and Donna. You're off to a good start. You have one hundred dollars. And now for our next question. What kind of books does Dave like? So Dave, what kind of books do you like? Donna, what kind of books does Dave like? All right, folks. Time's up! Donna, what kind of books does Dave like?

DONNA: Dave likes novels. He reads novels all the time.

RICH YOUNG: Dave, do you read novels all the time?

DAVE: Yes, I do.

RICH YOUNG: Dave and Donna, you now have two hundred dollars!

	Are you ready for the next question?
DONNA:	Ready, Rich.
DAVE:	Ready.
RICH YOUNG:	And the next question is: What kind of music does Donna like? So Donna, what kind of music do you like? Dave, what kind of music does Donna like? Okay, Dave and Donna. Time's up! Let's see your answers. Donna, what kind of music do you like?
DONNA:	I like jazz.
RICH YOUNG:	Dave, what kind of music does Donna like?
DAVE:	She doesn't like jazz. She likes ROCK music.
DONNA:	No, I don't.
DAVE:	Yes, you do.
RICH YOUNG:	Dave, she doesn't.
DAVE:	Yes, she does.
DONNA:	No, I don't.
RICH YOUNG:	Well, Donna and Dave, that's okay. You still have two hundred dollars, and we still have two more questions. Are you ready for the next question?
DAVE:	Ready.
DONNA:	I'm ready.
RICH YOUNG:	What is Dave's favorite sport? Dave, which sport do you really like? Donna, which sport does Dave like? Okay, Donna, let's see your answer. What is Dave's favorite sport?
DONNA:	Baseball.
RICH YOUNG:	And Dave? What's your favorite sport?
DAVE:	Football.
DONNA:	Football?! You don't like football!
DAVE:	Of course I do! I LOVE football!
DONNA:	No, you don't!

DAVE:	Yes, I do! I play football every Saturday!
DONNA:	No, you don't.
RICH YOUNG:	Okay, Dave and Donna. It's time for our last question. Are you ready? Well, I guess they are. The last question is: What is Donna's favorite kind of TV program? So Donna, what kind of TV programs do you like? Dave, what kind of TV programs does Donna like? All right, folks. Time is up! Dave, what kind of TV programs does Donna like?
DAVE:	Cartoons. Donna LOVES cartoons!
DONNA:	Cartoons??!! I don't like cartoons!
RICH YOUNG:	Donna, I'm almost afraid to ask. What's your answer?
DONNA:	News programs!
DAVE:	News programs?! Hah! I watch news programs. YOU watch cartoons!
DONNA:	No, I don't!
DAVE:	Yes, you do!
DONNA:	No, I don't!
DAVE:	Yes, you do!
DONNA:	No, I don't!
DAVE:	Rich, she does! She does! She really does!
DONNA:	Rich, don't listen to him!
RICH YOUNG:	Well, ladies and gentlemen, I'm afraid that's all the time there is. Remember, I don't care about your favorite movie, book, sport, or music . . . but I DO hope your favorite TV game show is *Family Favorites!* I'm your host, Rich Young, saying good-bye for now. See you next time.
ANNOUNCER:	*Family Favorites* is a Side by Side Television Production.

GRAMMAR

Simple Present Tense

| What kind of music | do | I we you they | like? |
| | does | he she it | |

| I We You They | like/don't like | jazz. |
| He She It | likes/doesn't like | |

Yes/No Questions

| Do | I we you they | like jazz? |
| Does | he she it | |

Short Answers

| Yes, | I we you they | do. |
| | he she it | does. |

| No, | I we you they | don't. |
| | he she it | doesn't. |

FUNCTIONS

Asking for and Reporting Information

Do you *go to the movies?*
  Yes, I do.
  No, I don't.

Inquiring about Likes/Dislikes

What kind of *movies* do you like?
Which *sports* do you like?

Do you like *comedies?*

Who is your favorite *actor?*
What's your favorite *sport?*

Expressing Likes

I like *novels.*
I love *hockey.*

He's great.

Pavarotti is my favorite.

Expressing Dislikes

I don't like *cartoons.*

Expressing Surprise–Disbelief

Football?!

Expressing Certainty

Hockey is definitely *my favorite sport.*

Hesitating

Hmm.
Let me see.

SEGMENT 16

- Daily Activities
- Object Pronouns
- Adverbs of Frequency
- Simple Present Tense

"She always calls, I usually write, we sometimes dance, we never fight . . . because we're Side by Side."

LESSON MENU

SBS-TV Backstage Bulletin Board

TO: Production Crew
Sets and props for this segment:

Kitchen
tables
chairs
glasses
telephone

Office
chairs
clock
desks
office supplies

Dorm Room
books
chair
desk
lamp

TO: Cast Members
Key words in this segment:

always
usually
sometimes
rarely
never

16.1 THERE'S THE PHONE! (13:55)

them	me	us	you	it	her	him

A. How often does your boyfriend call _____you_____¹?

B. He calls _____² every night. How often do you talk to your brother in college?

A. I talk to _____³ every Sunday.

B. My sister is in college, too. I talk to _____⁴ every Saturday.

A. Do you speak to your grandparents very often?

B. Yes. I call _____⁵ every weekend.

A. My grandparents call _____⁶ every Friday night.

B. There's the phone.

A. I'll get _____⁷. Hello.

C. ....

A. Oh hi, Uncle George! It's my Uncle George! How are you? It's so good to hear from

_____⁸! How's Aunt Sally?

C. ....

A. That's good. Please say "Hello" to _____⁹ from _____¹⁰.

What do you think Uncle George said on the telephone to his niece? Fill in
Uncle George's lines above.

How often do you speak to friends and family members on the telephone? Who are the
people you talk to?

....

....

16.2 SBS-TV ON LOCATION   (14:47)

SOUND CHECK

When do you watch TV?

100% always	90% usually	50% sometimes	10% rarely	0% never

1. a. usually
    (b.) always
    c. morning
    (d.) evening

2. a. always
    b. usually
    c. morning
    d. evening

3. a. sometimes
    b. always
    c. eight
    d. late

4. a. rarely
    b. nearly

5. a. ever
    b. never

Do you ever watch TV while you eat?

6. _____always_____

7. _____

8. _____

9. _____

10. _____

SEGMENT 16 •••••

31

16.3 SHE USUALLY STUDIES IN THE LIBRARY (15:12)

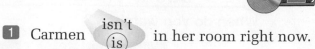

1 Carmen *isn't* / **is** in her room right now.

2 She **never** / *rarely* studies in her room.

3 She **usually** / *always* studies in the library.

16.4 SBS-TV ON LOCATION (15:22)

Do you sing in the shower?

1 I ____*never*____ sing in the shower.

2 I _____ sing in the shower.

3 I _____ sing in the shower.

Who washes the dishes in your household?

| wash | do | clean | cook |

I usually ____*wash*____¹ the dishes. Sometimes my

wife ____*washes*____² the dishes, but usually it's me.

My husband and I always _____³ the dishes together.

He rarely _____⁴ the dishes. I usually

_____⁵ them, and he dries them. We're a good team!

I never _____ [6] the dishes. My roommate always
_____ [7] them. I _____ [8] all the cooking. It's
a good arrangement. He _____ [9]. I _____ [10].

Do you snore when you sleep?

I _____rarely_____
snore when I sleep.

1

I _____
snore when I sleep.

2

I _____
snore when I sleep.

3

I _____
snore when I sleep.

4

I _____ snore,
but my husband _____
snores.

5

CLOSE-UP

Tell about YOUR household.

Who usually washes and dries the dishes? Who usually cooks?
Who usually cleans? Who usually does food shopping? How often?

16.5 I ALWAYS GET TO WORK ON TIME (16:33)

always	never	rarely	sometimes	usually

I _____always_____ [1] get to work on time.

I'm _____ [2] here by eight.

I _____ [3] get here early.

I _____ [4] get here late.

No, I _____ [5] get here late.

He _____ [6] gets to work on time.

He's _____ [7] here by eight.

He _____ [8] gets here early.

He _____ [9] gets here late.

No, I _____ [10] get here late!

Right! He _____ [11] gets here late!

WRITE YOUR OWN RAP!

Write a GrammarRap about yourself. Then write a GrammarRap about a friend.

Are you always on time for class or for work? Are you ever late?

GrammarRap about Me

I .... get to

.... on time.

I'm .... here by

....

I .... get here early.

I .... get here late.

No, I .... get here late!

GrammarRap about My Friend

He/She .... gets to

.... on time.

He's/She's .... here by

....

He/She .... gets here early.

He/She .... gets here late.

No, I .... get here late!

Right! He/She .... gets here late!

SCRAMBLED WORDS

There are some problems with the sound track. Fix the scrambled words.

1. Jenny **wlaysa** studies in the evening.   _always_

2. Andy **lyerar** calls his aunt and uncle.   _____

3. Bob **tsioemsme** watches TV after dinner.   _____

4. Bill and Helen **alulyus** eat lunch at work.   _____

5. Judy **venre** washes the dishes.   _____

WHAT'S MY LINE?

1. (wash)   I never ____wash____ the dishes. My husband usually _____ them.

2. (clean)   How often do you _____ your apartment?

3. (study)   My daughter usually _____ hard every night.

4. (watch)   I rarely _____ TV. My roommate _____ TV all the time!

5. (call)   I _____ my sister very often, and she _____ me a lot, too.

6. (get)   All the people in my office _____ to work on time. Do you usually

   _____ to work on time?

7. (sing)   My husband always _____ in the shower. My children _____
   in the shower, too.

8. (fix)   Who _____ things in your house when they're broken? I never

   _____ things around MY house.

9. (wash)   My next-door neighbor _____ his car every weekend. I never

   _____ my car! How about you? Do you _____ your car very
   often?

TELL ABOUT YOURSELF!

Complete the following. Then have a friend complete it and compare your answers.

I always ....   I rarely ....

I usually ....   I never ....

I sometimes ....

16.1 THERE'S THE PHONE! (13:55)

FRIEND 1: How often does your boyfriend call you?

FRIEND 2: He calls me every night. How often do you talk to your brother in college?

FRIEND 1: I talk to him every Sunday.

FRIEND 2: My sister is in college, too. I talk to her every Saturday.

FRIEND 1: Do you speak to your grandparents very often?

FRIEND 2: Yes. I call them every weekend.

FRIEND 1: My grandparents call us every Friday night.

FRIEND 2: There's the phone.

FRIEND 1: I'll get it. Hello. Oh hi, Uncle George!
(To her friend.)
It's my Uncle George!
(To Uncle on phone.)
How are you? It's so good to hear from you! How's Aunt Sally? That's good. Please say "Hello" to her from me.

ANNOUNCER: We're the telephone company. We bring people closer together.

16.2 SBS-TV ON LOCATION (14:47)

INTERVIEWER: When do you watch TV?

PERSON 1: I always watch TV in the evening.

PERSON 2: I usually watch TV in the morning.

PERSON 3: I sometimes watch TV late at night.

PERSON 4: I rarely watch TV.

PERSON 5: I never watch TV.

INTERVIEWER: Do you ever watch TV while you eat?

PERSON 6: Always.

PERSON 7: Usually.

PERSON 8: Sometimes.

PERSON 9: Rarely.

PERSON 10: Never.

16.3 SHE USUALLY STUDIES IN THE LIBRARY (15:12)

STUDENT 1: Does Carmen usually study in her room?

STUDENT 2: No. She rarely studies in her room. She usually studies in the library.

16.4 SBS-TV ON LOCATION (15:22)

INTERVIEWER: Do you sing in the shower?

PERSON 1: No. I never sing in the shower.

PERSON 2: Sing in the shower? Well, sometimes.

PERSON 3: I always sing in the shower! I sing opera! La . . . la-la-la-la-la-la-la-la-la!

INTERVIEWER: Who washes the dishes in your household?

PERSON 4: I usually wash the dishes. Sometimes my wife washes the dishes, but usually it's me.

PERSON 5: My husband and I always do the dishes together. He rarely washes the dishes. I usually wash them and he dries them. We're a good team!

PERSON 6: I never wash the dishes. My roommate always washes them. I do all the cooking. It's a good arrangement. He cleans. I cook.

INTERVIEWER: Do you snore when you sleep?

PERSON 7: Rarely.

PERSON 8: Snore? No! Never!

PERSON 9: Sometimes, I guess.

PERSON 10: Yes. I usually snore.

PERSON 11: I never snore. But my husband always snores. Sometimes it doesn't bother me at all, and sometimes it drives me crazy!

16.5 I ALWAYS GET TO WORK ON TIME—GrammarRap (16:33)

I always get to work on time.
I'm usually here by eight.
I sometimes get here early.
I never get here late.
No, I never get here late.

He always gets to work on time.
He's usually here by eight.
He sometimes gets here early.
He rarely gets here late.

No, I NEVER get here late!
Right! He NEVER gets here late!

GRAMMAR

Object Pronouns

He calls	me him her it us you them	every night.

Adverbs of Frequency

I	always usually sometimes rarely never	clean my apartment.

Simple Present Tense:
s vs. *non-s* Endings

I We You They	eat. read. wash.

He She It	eat**s**. read**s**. wash**es**.	[s] [z] [ɪz]

FUNCTIONS

Asking for and Reporting Information

How often *does your boyfriend call you?*
   He calls me every night.

Who *washes the dishes in your*
   household?
   I usually wash the dishes.
   My brother sometimes *washes them.*

Does *Carmen* usually *study in her room?*
   No. *She* rarely *studies in her room.*
   Yes. *She* usually *studies in the library.*

How's *Aunt Sally?*

When *do you watch TV?*
   I always watch TV in the morning.

Greeting People

Hello.
Hi, *Uncle George.*

SEGMENT 17

- **Describing People**
- **Have/Has**

"Dad has brown eyes, Mom's are blue. He looks like me.

She looks like you . . . Our family's Side by Side."

LESSON MENU

17.1 DID YOU HEAR THAT? (17:19)
Sound effects give clues about things people have.

17.2 MY SISTER AND I (19:10)
Two sisters tell how they are different.

SBS-TV Backstage Bulletin Board

TO: Production Crew
Sets and props for this segment:

Kitchen
counter
pet food

Living Room
sofa
coffee table

Doctor's Office
stethoscope
examining table

Bedroom
bed
toys

Dining Room
table
chairs

TO: Cast Members
Key words in this segment:

cat	talent	musical instrument
dog	motorcycle	house
mice	car	apartment
cockroach	eyes	piano
neighbor	hair	TV
problem	sister	friend
heart	different	
electric guitar	look like	

17.1 DID YOU HEAR THAT? (17:19)

WHAT DO THEY HAVE?

Circle the things that they have.

1
a. a pet
b. a dog
c. a cat

2
a. noisy neighbors
b. nosy neighbors
c. quiet neighbors

3
a. a problem with his heart
b. a very unusual heartbeat
c. a problem with his guitar

4
a. a new car
b. a very old car
c. a noisy car

5
a. a musical instrument
b. an electric guitar
c. musical talent

6
a. a bicycle
b. a motorcycle
c. a car

7
a. cockroaches
b. mice
c. a cat

CLOSE-UP

1 Do you have a dog?   Yes, I do.   No, I don't.

2 Do you have a cat?   Yes, I do.   No, I don't.

3 Do you have a new car?   Yes, I do.   No, I don't.

4 Do you have a motorcycle?   Yes, I do.   No, I don't.

5 Do you have noisy neighbors?   Yes, I do.   No, I don't.

6 Do you have a musical instrument?   Yes, I do.   No, I don't.

7 What other things do you have?   ....

....

The sound editor needs help. Match the sound effects with the scenes below.

a. **Meow!**	b. *CRASH!*	c. *Thump Thump!*
d. Honk Honk!	e. **Bow Wow!**	f. *squeak squeak!*

1 ___f___   2 _____   3 _____

4 _____   5 _____   6 _____

WHAT'S MY LINE?

	Do	Does	have	has	
I	he	she	it	we	they

1 _____Do_____ you _____ a musical instrument?

Yes, _____ _____ a guitar.

2 _____ Barbara _____ a sister?

No, but _____ _____ three brothers.

3 _____ you and your wife _____ a car?

Yes, _____ _____ an old car.

4 _____ your apartment _____ a dining room?

No, but _____ _____ a very large kitchen.

5 _____ your neighbors _____ a pet?

Yes, _____ _____ a very noisy dog.

6 _____ your son _____ problems at school?

Yes, _____ _____ problems with English.

17.2 MY SISTER AND I (19:10)

has	long	brown	apartment	color	friends	sisters	I'm
have	short		two bicycle	dog	guitar	don't	

SISTERS 1 & 2:   My sister and I look very different.

SISTER 1:   I have blue eyes and she _____ [1]

_____ [2] eyes.

SISTER 2:   I _____ [3] short hair and she

_____ [4] _____ [5] hair.

SISTER 1:   _____ [6] tall.

SISTER 2:   And I'm _____ [7].

SISTERS 1 & 2:   As you can see, I _____ [8] look like my sister. We look very different.

SISTER 1:   I _____ [9] a house and she _____ [10] an _____ [11].

SISTER 2:   She _____ [12] a cat and I _____ [13] a _____ [14].

SISTERS 1 & 2:   We both _____ [15] musical instruments.

SISTER 1:   I _____ [16] a piano and she _____ [17] a _____ [18].

SISTER 2:   She _____ [19] a car and I _____ [20] a _____ [21].

SISTER 1:   I have a black-and-white TV and she _____ [22] a _____ [23] TV.

SISTER 2:   She _____ [24] a lot of friends and I _____ [25] just one or

_____ [26].

SISTER 1 & 2:   As you can see, we're very different. But we're _____ [27], and

we're _____ [28].

WHICH SISTER?

1. She has (blue (brown)) eyes.

2. She has (blue   brown) eyes.

3. She has (short   long) hair.

4. She has (short   long) hair.

5. She's (tall   short).

6. She's (tall   short).

7. She has (a house   an apartment).

8. She has (a house   an apartment).

9. She has a (cat   dog).

10. She has a (cat   dog).

11. She has a (piano   guitar).

12. She has a (piano   guitar).

13. She has a (car   bicycle).

14. She has a (car   bicycle).

15. She has a (black-and-white   color) TV.

16. She has a (black-and-white   color) TV.

17. She has (a lot of   just one or two) friends.

18. She has (a lot of   just one or two) friends.

CLOSE-UP

You're on Side by Side TV! Tell about yourself. What color eyes do you have? Do you have short hair or long hair? Are you tall or short? Do you live in a house or an apartment? Do you have any pets? Do you have any musical instruments? Then tell about someone else—a friend, a family member, or even a famous person! How are you different?

....

....

....

....

....

....

....

TV CROSSWORD

Across →

1. How often do you _____ to the movies?

5. We live in a nice _____.

8. I'm noisy, and my brother _____ quiet.

9. Do you have _____ hair?

10. My father and I both have brown _____.

12. Our children both have short _____.

13. Do your parents have noisy neighbors?

    Yes, _____ do.

14. Do I have a problem with my _____?

17. I _____ on the telephone a lot.

18. My apartment has _____!

19. My daughter has _____ eyes.

Down ↓

1. My brother has an electric _____.

2. Do you have a car or a _____?

3. _____ your son have a dog?

4. My sister _____ a very old bicycle.

6. The _____ is my favorite musical instrument.

7. Pavarotti has great musical _____.

11. My mother is tall, and I'm _____.

14. Mr. and Mrs. Smith _____ a new car.

15. Is she short or _____?

16. I write to _____ every week.

17.1 DID YOU HEAR THAT? (17:19)

FRIEND 1: Do you have a dog?
FRIEND 2: No. I have a cat.

VISITOR: Do you have quiet neighbors?
WIFE: No. We have noisy neighbors.

PATIENT: Well, Doctor, do I have a problem with my heart?
DOCTOR: Yes. You have a VERY unusual heartbeat.
PATIENT: Oh, my!

BOY 1: Do your parents have a new car?
BOY 2: No. They have a very old car.

WIFE 1: Does your son have a musical instrument?
HUSBAND 2: Yes. He has an electric guitar.
WIFE 2: He has great musical talent. Don't you think so?
HUSBAND 1: Oh, yes. He does.
WIFE 1: Definitely!

FRIEND 1: Does your daughter have a car?
FRIEND 2: No. She has a motorcycle.

FRIEND 3: Does your apartment have cockroaches?
FRIEND 4: No. It has mice.

17.2 MY SISTER AND I (19:10)

SISTERS 1 & 2: My sister and I look very different.

SISTER 1: I have blue eyes and she has brown eyes.
SISTER 2: I have short hair and she has long hair.
SISTER 1: I'm tall.
SISTER 2: And I'm short.
SISTERS 1 & 2: As you can see, I don't look like my sister. We look very different.
SISTER 1: I have a house and she has an apartment.
SISTER 2: She has a cat and I have a dog.
SISTERS 1 & 2: We both have musical instruments.
SISTER 1: I have a piano and she has a guitar.
SISTER 2: She has a car and I have a bicycle.
SISTER 1: I have a black-and-white TV and she has a color TV.
SISTER 2: She has a lot of friends and I have just one or two.
SISTERS 1 & 2: As you can see, we're very different. But we're sisters, and we're friends.

GRAMMAR

Have/Has

I We You They	have	brown eyes.
He She It	has	

FUNCTIONS

Asking for and Reporting Information

Do you have *quiet neighbors?*

I have *a house.*
She has *an apartment.*

Describing

We *have noisy neighbors.*
They *have a very old car.*

My sister and I look very different.
I don't look like *my sister.*

We're very different.

I have *blue* eyes.
She has *brown* eyes.

I have *short* hair.
She has *long* hair.

I'm *tall.*

Expressing Certainty

Definitely!

Expressing Surprise–Disbelief

Oh, my!

Inquiring about Agreement

Don't you think so?

SEGMENT 18

- **Feelings and Emotions**
- **Simple Present vs. Present Continuous**
- **Adjectives**

"No one's angry, no one's sad, we're all happy

and we're glad . . . to be Side by Side."

LESSON MENU

SBS-TV Backstage Bulletin Board

TO: Production Crew
Sets and props for this segment:

Living Room
    chair
    rocking chair
    sofa
    television

Theater
    director's chair

TO: Cast Members
Key words for this segment:

bite	angry	nervous
cry	cold	sad
giggle	embarrassed	sick
perspire	happy	thirsty
shiver	hot	tired
shout	hungry	
smile		
whistle		
yawn		

18.1 I ALWAYS CRY WHEN I'M SAD (20:13)

SOUND CHECK

I	I'm	cry	crying

Why are you _____crying_____ [1]?

_____ _____ [2] because I'm sad.

_____ [3] always _____ [4] when

_____ [5] sad.

18.2 WE ALWAYS SHIVER WHEN WE'RE COLD (20:33)

SOUND CHECK

We	we're	shiver	shivering

Why are you _____shivering_____ [1]?

_____ _____ [2] because we're cold.

_____ [3] always _____ [4] when

_____ [5] cold.

TELL ME WHY!

he	she	they
he's	she's	they're

blush	sing	dance

_He's_ [1] blushing

because he's embarrassed.

_____ [2] always

_____ [3] when

_____ [4] embarrassed.

_____ [5] singing

because _____ [6] happy.

_____ [7] always

_____ [8] when

_____ [9] happy.

_____ [10] dancing

because _____ [11] happy.

_____ [12] always

_____ [13] when

_____ [14] happy.

SOUND CHECK

| I | I'm | ask | leave | shout | yawn |

Why are you _____yawning_____ 1?

Who's there?

It's me.

You?

Yes. Why are you _____ 2?

I'm _____ 3 because _____ 4 tired. _____ 5 always _____ 6 when _____ 7 tired. And why are you _____ 8 me questions?

I always _____ 9 questions. It's my job.

Well, please _____ 10 right now! Go! Get out of here!

Why are you _____ 11?

I'm _____ 12 because _____ 13 angry. _____ 14 always _____ 15 when _____ 16 angry. Now please _____ 17! Go! Good-bye! And take your little word with you!

Okay. We're _____ 18. Sorry to bother you.

Hmm!

18.4 THE AUDITION (21:35)

> **WHICH WORD?**

Help the video editor match the action with the correct adjective.

angry	cold	embarrassed	happy	hot	hungry
nervous		sad	sick	thirsty	tired

1. _____nervous_____   2. _____   3. _____   4. _____

5. _____   6. _____   7. _____   8. _____

9. _____   10. _____   11. _____

> **WHAT'S MY LINE?**

thirsty	cold	angry	happy	nervous	hot	hungry

1. Please open the window. It's very _____hot_____ in here.

2. I'm _____. Let's eat!

3. I'm shouting because I'm _____.

4. Close the window. It's _____!

5. Wendy is _____ today. It's her birthday.

6. I'm really _____. Is there any lemonade in the refrigerator?

7. William has a job interview tomorrow, and he's very _____.

18.5 SBS-TV ON LOCATION (22:51)

SCRAMBLED SOUND TRACK

The sound track is all mixed up. Put the words in the correct order.

a I'm . nervous , giggle I When   _When I'm nervous, I giggle._

b angry I . shout When I'm ,   _____

c I'm smile . When , happy I   _____

d nails I . When nervous bite I'm , my   _____

e get never angry . I   _____

f turns angry red . When my , I'm face   _____

g happy I'm When sing I . ,   _____

h When . nervous , I'm perspire I   _____

i happy When I whistle I'm . ,   _____

MATCH THE LINES

Match the scrambled sound track above with the people in the interviews.

1 _d_   **2** ___   **3** ___

4 ___   **5** ___   **6** ___

7 ___   **8** ___   **9** ___

18.6 I SMILE WHEN I'M HAPPY (23:38)

FINISH THE RAP!

blush	frown	shout	smile	embarrassed	mad
blushing	frowning	shouting	smiling	happy	sad

I _____smile_____¹ when I'm happy.

I _____² when I'm sad.

I _____³ when I'm embarrassed.

And I _____⁴ when I'm mad.

Are you _____⁵?
  Yes. I'm happy.

Are you _____⁶?
  Yes. I'm sad.

  Are you _____⁷?
I'm embarrassed.

  Are you _____⁸?
Yes. I'm mad.

We smile when we're _____⁹.

We frown when we're _____¹⁰.

We blush when we're _____¹¹.

And we shout when we're _____¹².

We _____¹³ when we're happy.

We _____¹⁴ when we're sad.

We _____¹⁵ when we're embarrassed.

And we _____¹⁶ when we're mad.

WRITE YOUR OWN RAP!

I .... when I'm ....

I .... when I'm ....

I .... when I'm ....

And I .... when I'm ....

WHY ARE THEY FEELING THIS WAY?

1. The students in my English class are happy today because ....

....

2. Betty is nervous today because ....

....

3. My neighbors are angry because ....

....

4. I'm very tired because ....

....

5. All my friends are sad today because ....

....

6. I'm embarrassed because ....

....

WHAT'S MY LINE?

1. When **I / I'm** nervous, I bite my nails.

2. Oh, really? I never **bite / biting** my nails.

3. I'm **smile / smiling** because I'm very happy.

4. I also **smile / smiling** when I'm happy.

5. When I'm angry, my face **turns / is turning** red.

6. Look! Your face **is turning / turns** red now!

7. **I relax / I'm relaxing** because I'm tired.

8. When I'm tired, I **sleeping / sleep**.

9. **I / I'm** usually cry when I'm sad.

10. I never **crying / cry**.

11. Why are you **giggle / giggling**?

12. **I / I'm** nervous.

13. Why are you **ask / asking** me questions?

14. I always **asking / ask** questions!

18.1   I ALWAYS CRY WHEN I'M SAD

(20:13)

ANNOUNCER: Tune in tomorrow for another episode of *Our Children, Our Lives.*

INTERVIEWER: Why are you crying?

SAD MAN: I'm crying because I'm sad. I always cry when I'm sad.

18.2   WE ALWAYS SHIVER WHEN WE'RE COLD   (20:33)

INTERVIEWER: Why are you shivering?

WIFE: We're shivering because we're cold. We always shiver when we're cold.

18.3   WHO'S THERE?   (20:42)

INTERVIEWER: Why are you yawning?

TIRED LADY: Who's there?

INTERVIEWER: It's me.

TIRED LADY: You?

INTERVIEWER: Yes. Why are you yawning?

TIRED LADY: I'm yawning because I'm tired. I always yawn when I'm tired. And why are you asking me questions?

INTERVIEWER: I always ask questions. It's my job.

ANGRY LADY: Well, please leave right now! Go! Get out of here!

INTERVIEWER: Why are you shouting?

ANGRY LADY: I'm shouting because I'm angry. I always shout when I'm angry. Now please leave! Go! Good-bye! And take your little word with you!

INTERVIEWER: Okay. We're leaving. Sorry to bother you.

ANGRY LADY: Hmm!

18.4   THE AUDITION   (21:35)

DIRECTOR: All right. Who's next?

ACTOR: I am.

DIRECTOR: Oh, I remember you. Your name is Benny.

ACTOR: Lenny. Lenny Thomas.

DIRECTOR: All right, Lenny. I'm going to give you some adjectives . . .

ACTOR: More adjectives?

DIRECTOR: Yes . . . and you're going to act them out. Okay?

ACTOR: Yes. I'm ready.

DIRECTOR: Then let's begin. "Nervous." "Sad." "Happy." "Tired." "Sick." "Cold." "Hot." "Hungry." "Thirsty." "Angry." "Embarrassed." All right. Very good, Lenny. Thank you.

ACTOR: Is that all?
DIRECTOR: Yes, that's all. Thank you.
            Next!

18.5   SBS-TV ON LOCATION   (22:51)

INTERVIEWER: What do you do when you're
               nervous?
PERSON 1:   I bite my nails.
PERSON 2:   When I'm nervous? Let me
               see. I perspire.
PERSON 3:   I giggle. I guess I'm nervous
               now.

INTERVIEWER: What do you do when you're
               angry?
PERSON 4:   I shout.
PERSON 5:   When I'm angry, my face turns
               red.
PERSON 6:   Hmm. I don't know. I never
               get angry.

INTERVIEWER: What do you do when you're
               happy?
PERSON 7:   I whistle.
PERSON 8:   What do I do when I'm happy?
               That's easy. I smile.
PERSON 9:   When I'm happy, I sing! Like
               this: la-la-la-la!

18.6   I SMILE WHEN I'M HAPPY—

GrammarRap   (23:38)

I smile when I'm happy.
I frown when I'm sad.
   I blush when I'm embarrassed.
   And I shout when I'm mad.

Are you smiling?
   Yes. I'm happy.
Are you frowning?
   Yes. I'm sad.
   Are you blushing?
I'm embarrassed.
   Are you shouting?
Yes. I'm mad.

We smile when we're happy.
We frown when we're sad.
We blush when we're embarrassed.
And we shout when we're mad.

We smile when we're happy.
We frown when we're sad.
We blush when we're embarrassed.
And we shout when we're mad.

GRAMMAR

Simple Present Tense

I always **cry** when I'm sad.
I never **wash** the dishes.

Present Continuous Tense

I'm crying because I'm sad.
I'm singing because I'm happy.

Adjectives

I'm	angry.	hot.	sick.
	cold.	hungry.	thirsty.
	embarrassed.	nervous.	tired.
	happy.	sad.	

FUNCTIONS

Asking for and Reporting Information

Why are you *crying?*
    I'm *crying* because *I'm sad.*

Describing Feelings–Emotions

I'm *angry/cold/embarrassed/happy/hot/hungry/*
    nervous/sad/sick/thirsty/tired.

When I'm *nervous,* I *bite my nails.*

Apologizing

Sorry to *bother you.*

- Describing Activities
- Simple Present vs. Present Continuous

"They're doing funny things today. They never do these things this way . . . They're Side by Side."

LESSON MENU

19.1   I'M WASHING THE DISHES IN THE BATHTUB   (24:38)
Someone is very surprised when she sees what her friend is doing.

19.2   SPARKLE FLOOR CLEANER   (25:13)
One friend convinces another to switch from Ordinary Soap to Sparkle.

19.3   WHAT ARE THEY DOING?—GrammarRap   (25:54)
The GrammarRappers magically appear in an office, a kitchen, and a backyard.

SBS-TV Backstage Bulletin Board

TO: Production Crew

Sets and props for this segment:

Bathroom
bathtub
dishes
dishwashing liquid
rubber duck

Kitchen
bucket
mop
floor cleaner

Office
desk
lamp
clock

Kitchen
stove
pot
spaghetti

Yard
cat
tub

TO: Cast Members

Key words in this segment:

bathtub	bathe	broken
cat	cook	sorry
dishes	shine	strange
floor	wash	late
sink	work	always
soap		never
spaghetti		usually

19.1 I'M WASHING THE DISHES IN THE BATHTUB (24:38)

EDITING MIX-UP

The video editor made a mistake! Put the following lines in the correct order.

_____ That's strange! Do you USUALLY wash the dishes in the bathtub?

_____ Why are you doing THAT?!

__1__ What are you doing?!

_____ Because my sink is broken.

_____ I'm sorry to hear that.

_____ No. I NEVER wash the dishes in the bathtub,
but I'm washing the dishes in the bathtub TODAY.

_____ I'm washing the dishes in the bathtub.

SOUND CHECK

A. What [are / do]¹ you [do / doing]²?!

B. [I / I'm]³ [wash / washing]⁴ the dishes in the bathtub.

A. [That's / What's]⁵ strange! [Are / Do]⁶ you USUALLY [wash / washing]⁷ the dishes in the bathtub?

B. No. [I / I'm]⁸ NEVER [wash / washing]⁹ the dishes in the bathtub,

but [I / I'm]¹⁰ [wash / washing]¹¹ the dishes in the bathtub [TODAY / TUESDAY]¹².

A. Why [are / do]¹³ you [do / doing]¹⁴ THAT?!

B. Because my sink [is / it's]¹⁵ broken.

A. [I / I'm]¹⁶ sorry to [ear / hear]¹⁷ that.

19.2 SPARKLE FLOOR CLEANER (25:13)

EDITING MIX-UP

The video editor made a mistake! Put the following lines in the correct order.

_____ But you're using "Ordinary Soap!!"

_____ Never! I use "Sparkle." Here, Tim. I have some with me. Let's try it on your floor right now.

__1__ Hi, Tim!

_____ No more "Ordinary Soap" for me!

_____ Wow! Look at this floor! It's shining!

_____ Tim!! What are you doing?

_____ Floors always shine with "Sparkle!"

_____ Oh hi, Charles!

_____ I'm washing my kitchen floor.

_____ It always shines with "Sparkle!"

_____ So? I always use "Ordinary Soap." Don't YOU use "Ordinary Soap" when you wash YOUR kitchen floor?

WHAT'S THE LINE?

brush	drink	feed	wash
brushing	drinking	feeding	washing

1 Why are you _____washing_____ your hair with "Ordinary Shampoo?" I always _____ my hair with "Dazzle Shampoo."

2 Why are you _____ "Ordinary Coffee?" I never _____ "Ordinary Coffee." I _____ "Roaster's Choice."

3 But you're _____ your teeth with "Ordinary Toothpaste!" Why don't you _____ with "Smilodent?"

4 My dog is very important to me, so I always _____ him "Peppy Dog Food." How about you? What are you _____ your dog today?

WRITE YOUR OWN COMMERCIAL!

Using the following as a guide, write a commercial for a cleaning product and practice it with a friend.

A. Hi, ...!
(friend's name)

B. Oh hi, ...!
(your name)

A. ....!! What are you doing?
(friend's name)

B. I'm ....ing my ....

A. But you're using "..!!"
(name of friend's cleaning product)

B. So? I always use "..." Don't YOU use
(name of friend's cleaning product)

"..." when you ....
(name of friend's cleaning product)

YOUR ....?

A. Never! I use "..." Here, ...
(name of your cleaning product)   (friend's name)

I have some with me. Let's try it on your .... right now.

B. Wow! Look at (this/these) ....! (It's/They're) shining!

A. (It/They) ALWAYS (shines/shine) with "..!"
(name of your cleaning product)

B. No more "..." for me!
(name of friend's cleaning product)

A. ....s ALWAYS shine with "..!"
(name of your cleaning product)

60

19.3 WHAT ARE THEY DOING? (25:54)

FINISH THE RAP!

always	bathing	cooks	cooking	doing	he	he's	his
it's	late	on	that	what's	why's	works	working

What's Fran ___doing___ ¹?

  She's _____ ² late.

Working _____ ³?

Why's she _____ ⁴ that?

  It's Monday. She always _____ ⁵ late
  on Monday.

  _____ ⁶ Bob doing?

  _____ ⁷ cooking spaghetti.

  _____ ⁸ spaghetti?

Why's _____ ⁹ doing _____ ¹⁰?

  It's Wednesday. _____ ¹¹ always

  _____ ¹² spaghetti _____ ¹³
  Wednesday.

What's Gary _____ ¹⁴?

  _____ ¹⁵ bathing _____ ¹⁶ cat.

_____ ¹⁷ _____ ¹⁸ cat?

_____ ¹⁹ he doing that?

_____ ²⁰ Friday. He _____ ²¹

bathes _____ ²² cat on Friday.

WRITE YOUR OWN RAP!

What are you doing?

  I'm ....

....? Why are you doing that?

  It's .... I always ....

  on ....

WRONG LINE

Cross out the mistakes.

1 Mary always ~~study~~ ~~studying~~ studies English ~~on~~ at ~~in~~ Sunday.

2 ~~She~~ She's ~~Her~~ bathing the ~~dog~~ cat ~~dishes~~.

3 They're cleaning their house ~~today~~ ~~usually~~ right now.

4 ~~Are~~ Do ~~Does~~ you usually ~~eat~~ eats ~~eating~~ breakfast?

5 Our children never ~~watch~~ watches ~~watching~~ TV ~~on~~ ~~Monday~~ Wednesday ~~today~~.

6 Floors always ~~shine~~ shines ~~shining~~ with "Sparkle."

7 But ~~you~~ you're ~~your~~ using "Ordinary Soap!"

8 Why's ~~he~~ they ~~you~~ doing that?

SCRAMBLED SOUND TRACK

The sound track is all mixed up. Put the words in the correct order.

1 | apartment | always | cleans | . | on | He | his | Friday |

He always cleans his apartment on Friday.

2 | in | the | usually | you | Do | dishes | the | ? | wash | bathtub |

_____

3 | to | her | walking | . | bicycle | school | is | because | She's | broken |

_____

4 | I | working | late | never | but | I'm | today | late | work | , | . |

_____

5 | spaghetti | ? | cook | Does | on | usually | he | Wednesday |

_____

6 | "Ordinary Soap?" | Why | washing | dishes | are | with | your | you |

_____

19.1 I'M WASHING THE DISHES IN THE BATHTUB (24:38)

FRIEND 1: What are you doing?!

FRIEND 2: I'm washing the dishes in the bathtub.

FRIEND 1: That's strange! Do you USUALLY wash the dishes in the bathtub?

FRIEND 2: No. I NEVER wash the dishes in the bathtub, but I'm washing the dishes in the bathtub TODAY.

FRIEND 1: Why are you doing THAT?!

FRIEND 2: Because my sink is broken.

FRIEND 1: I'm sorry to hear that.

19.2 SPARKLE FLOOR CLEANER (25:13)

CHARLES: Hi, Tim!

TIM: Oh hi, Charles!

CHARLES: Tim!! What are you doing?

TIM: I'm washing my kitchen floor.

CHARLES: But you're using "Ordinary Soap!!"

TIM: So? I always use "Ordinary Soap." Don't YOU use "Ordinary Soap" when you wash YOUR kitchen floor?

CHARLES: Never! I use "Sparkle." Here, Tim. I have some with me. Let's try it on your floor right now.

(Charles pours some "Sparkle" on the floor and takes the mop from Tim's hands.)

TIM: Wow! Look at this floor! It's shining!

CHARLES: It always shines with "Sparkle!"

TIM: No more "Ordinary Soap" for me!

ANNOUNCER: Floors always shine with "Sparkle!"

19.3 WHAT ARE THEY DOING?— GrammarRap (25:54)

What's Fran doing?
  She's working late.
Working late?
Why's she doing that?
  It's Monday.
  She always works late on Monday.

What's Bob doing?
  He's cooking spaghetti.
Cooking spaghetti?
Why's he doing that?
  It's Wednesday.
  He always cooks spaghetti on Wednesday.

What's Gary doing?
  He's bathing his cat.
Bathing his cat?
Why's he doing that?
  It's Friday.
  He always bathes his cat on Friday.

GRAMMAR

Simple Present Tense

> I never **wash** the dishes in the bathtub.

Present Continuous Tense

> I**'m washing** the dishes in the bathtub today.

FUNCTIONS

Asking for and Reporting Information

What are you doing?
    I'm *washing the dishes in the bathtub.*

Do you usually *wash the dishes in the bathtub?*

My *sink* is broken.

Expressing Surprise–Disbelief

That's strange!

Wow!

Sympathizing

I'm sorry to hear that.

Expressing Approval

Look at this *floor!* It's *shining!*

Asking for Clarification

So?

SEGMENT 20

- **Expressing Ability**
- **Occupations**
- **Can**

"They can dance and they can sing. They can do most anything . . . together Side by Side."

LESSON MENU

SBS-TV Backstage Bulletin Board

TO: Production Crew
Sets and props for this segment:

United Nations	Auto Shop
sign	car
	tools

Employment Agency
chairs
computer
desk

TO: Cast Members
Key words in this segment:

actor	Chinese	drive
baker	Spanish	cook
bus driver	Japanese	type
chef	Korean	teach
dancer	Portuguese	paint
mechanic		dance
painter	sing	write
secretary	play	act
teacher	speak	
truck driver	fix	
writer	bake	

SOUND CHECK

Can you sing?

can   can't

1 Yes, I _____can_____.

2 No, I _____.

You see, I _____ sing.

Can you play the violin?

3 Yes, I _____.

4 No, I _____. I'm sorry.

I just _____ play the violin.

WHAT CAN THEY DO?

1 Can she ski?

   a. Yes, she can.

   b. No, she can't.

2 Can he drive?

   a. Yes, he can.

   b. No, he can't.

3 Can they dance?

   a. Yes, they can.

   b. No, they can't.

4 Can he type?

   a. Yes, he can.

   b. No, he can't.

5 Can she swim?

   a. Yes, she can.

   b. No, she can't.

6 Can they cook?

   a. Yes, they can.

   b. No, they can't.

20.2 CAN YOU? (28:25)

A. _____Can_____[1] you speak Hungarian?

B. No, I _____[2]. But I _____[3] speak Romanian.

20.3 SBS-TV ON LOCATION (28:32)

INFORMATION CHECK

Circle the statements that are true about each person.

1   a. He can't speak English.

     (b.) He can speak English.

     (c.) He can speak Chinese.

2   a. He can't speak Chinese.

     b. He can't speak Spanish.

     c. He can speak Spanish.

3   a. She can't speak Japanese.

     b. She can speak Japanese.

     c. She can't speak Spanish.

4   a. He can't speak Korean.

     b. He can speak Japanese.

     c. He can't speak Japanese.

5   a. She can't speak Korean.

     b. She can't speak Portuguese.

     c. She can speak Portuguese.

6   a. She can speak today.

     b. She can't speak today.

     c. She can speak English.

CLOSE-UP

What languages can YOU speak?

20.4 OF COURSE THEY CAN (28:59)

SCRAMBLED SOUND TRACK

The sound track is all mixed up. Put the words in the correct order.

fix	course	a	.
cars	every	?	.
Of	Jack	He	
Can	mechanic		
He's	can	cars	
he	fixes	day	!

A. _____Can Jack fix cars?_____

B. _____

_____

_____

_____

_____

SCRIPT CHECK

Help the cast rehearse important words in this segment.

| baker | chef | painter | teacher | |
| bus driver | dancer | secretary | truck driver | writer |

1. Mario bakes very well. He's a _____baker_____.

2. Paul drives a truck. He's a _____.

3. Linda teaches. She's a _____.

4. Alberto can cook. He's a _____.

5. Sam can paint. He's a _____.

6. Julie writes very well. She's a _____.

7. Frank drives a bus. He's a _____.

8. Gloria dances very well. She's a _____.

9. Irene can type. She's a _____.

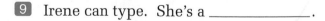

20.5 SO YOU'RE LOOKING FOR A JOB (29:25)

SCENE CHECK

What things **can** *this job applicant do? What* **can't** *he do?*

1 He ((can)   can't) fix cars.

2 He (can   can't) bake bread and cakes.

3 He (can   can't) bake chocolate chip cookies.

4 He (can   can't) drive a bus.

5 He (can   can't) drive a car.

6 He (can   can't) cook.

7 He (can   can't) type.

8 He (can   can't) teach.

9 He (can   can't) paint.

10 He (can   can't) drive a truck.

11 He (can   can't) dance.

12 He (can   can't) write.

13 He (can   can't) act.

EDITING MIX-UP

The video editor made a mistake! Put each pair of lines in the correct order.

1 _2_ I can fix cars.

 _1_ Tell me, what can you do?

2 ____ Yes, that's right.

 ____ Oh. You're a mechanic!

3 ____ Can you do anything else?

 ____ Well . . . I can do lots of things, I guess.

4 ____ No, I can't.

 ____ Can you bake bread and cakes?

5 ____ I can drive a car, but I can't drive a bus.

 ____ That's too bad.

6 ____ Oh, no! I can't cook at all!

 ____ Can you cook?

7 ____ I can't drive a truck.

 ____ This company is looking for a truck driver.

8 ____ Thank you.

 ____ Believe me, you can act. You're a terrific actor.

GOOD NEWS OR BAD NEWS?

Do these lines indicate "good news" or "bad news"?

1. "I can fix cars." Good news Bad news

2. "I'm afraid we don't have any jobs for mechanics right now." Good news Bad news

3. "I can do lots of things, I guess." Good news Bad news

4. "I'm sure we can find a job that's right for you." Good news Bad news

5. "I'm afraid I can't." Good news Bad news

6. "Oh, no! I can't cook at all!" Good news Bad news

7. "Here's a job for a secretary." Good news Bad news

8. "Sorry. I can't." Good news Bad news

9. "No, definitely not. I can't paint." Good news Bad news

10. "You can act!" Good news Bad news

11. "I think you can get the job." Good news Bad news

TO BE OR NOT TO BE AN ACTOR!

Look at the pictures and perform the scene . . . very dramatically!

This is terrible! I can't believe this!

I can't do ANYTHING!! Woe is me! What can I do?!
What can I do? What can I do?

CAN THEY OR CAN'T THEY?

1. Ben _____can_____ type. He's a very good _____secretary_____.

2. I _____can't_____ write very well at all. I'm not a very good writer.

3. Olivia _____ bake bread and cakes. She's an excellent _____.

4. I'm not a very good _____. I _____ teach anything!

5. Jim is an excellent _____. He _____ fix any problem with a car.

6. I'm a _____. I _____ drive big trucks and small trucks.

7. Pierre is a _____ at a restaurant. He _____ cook delicious meals.

8. I'm a very bad _____. I _____ paint at all!

SURVEY

Which of these things can you do? Answer "Yes, I can" or "No, I can't."

1. Can you drive? ....
2. Can you cook? ....
3. Can you sing? ....
4. Can you dance? ....
5. Can you swim? ....
6. Can you ski? ....
7. Can you skate? ....

8. Can you draw? ....
9. Can you play the guitar? ....
10. Can you play basketball? ....
11. Can you ride a bicycle? ....
12. Can you ride a horse? ....
13. Can you type? ....
14. Can you use a computer? ....

INTERVIEW

Make up five questions and then interview two friends. What can your friends do?

	Friend 1	Friend 2
1. Can you _____?	....	....
2. Can you _____?	....	....
3. Can you _____?	....	....
4. Can you _____?	....	....
5. Can you _____?	....	....

20.1   SBS-TV ON LOCATION   (27:20)

INTERVIEWER:	Can you sing?
PERSON 1:	Yes, I can.
	(Singing.)
	People, people who need people, are the luckiest people in the world.
	(Asking Interviewer.)
	How's that?
INTERVIEWER:	Very nice.
INTERVIEWER:	Can you sing?
PERSON 2:	No, I can't.
	(Singing.)
	Feelings . . . nothing more than feelings . . .
	(To Interviewer.)
	You see? I can't sing. Sorry.
INTERVIEWER:	That's okay.
INTERVIEWER:	Can you play the violin?
PERSON 3:	Yes, I can.

(Person 3 plays the violin.)

INTERVIEWER:	That's beautiful!
PERSON 3:	Thank you.
INTERVIEWER:	Can you play the violin?
PERSON 4:	No, I can't.

(Person 4 plays the violin.)

PERSON 4:	I'm sorry. I just can't play the violin.
INTERVIEWER:	That's all right.

20.2   CAN YOU?   (28:25)

DIPLOMAT 1:	Can you speak Hungarian?
DIPLOMAT 2:	No, I can't. But I can speak Romanian.

20.3   SBS-TV ON LOCATION   (28:32)

INTERVIEWER:	What languages can you speak?
PERSON 1:	I can speak English and Chinese.
PERSON 2:	I can't speak Chinese, but I can speak Spanish.
PERSON 3:	I can't speak Spanish, but I can speak Japanese.
PERSON 4:	Japanese? No. I can't speak Japanese, but I CAN speak Korean.
PERSON 5:	No. I'm afraid I can't speak Korean, but I can speak Portuguese.
PERSON 6:	I can't speak anything today. I have laryngitis. Sorry.

20.4   OF COURSE THEY CAN   (28:59)

CUSTOMER:	Can Jack fix cars?
MANAGER:	Of course he can. He fixes cars every day. He's a mechanic!

20.5 SO YOU'RE LOOKING FOR A JOB (29:25)

AGENCY OWNER: So you're looking for a job.

JOB SEEKER: Yes, I am.

AGENCY OWNER: Well, tell me, what can you do?

JOB SEEKER: I can fix cars.

AGENCY OWNER: Oh. You're a mechanic!

JOB SEEKER: Yes, that's right.

AGENCY OWNER: Well, let's see if we can find a job for a mechanic. Hmm . . . I'm afraid we don't have any jobs for mechanics right now. Can you do anything else?

JOB SEEKER: Hmm. Well . . . I can do lots of things, I guess.

AGENCY OWER: Such as?

JOB SEEKER: Well, I . . . I can . . . uh . . . I can . . . Hmm.

AGENCY OWNER: Tell you what. Let's check and see what kinds of jobs we have right now. I'm sure we can find a job that's right for you.

JOB SEEKER: Thank you.

AGENCY OWNER: Let me see. Oh, here we are. Betty's Bakery is looking for a baker. Can you bake bread and cakes?

JOB SEEKER: No, I can't. I can bake chocolate chip cookies, but I can't bake bread or cakes.

AGENCY OWNER: All right. Let's see what else we have. Ah! The Ajax Bus Company is looking for a bus driver. Can you drive a bus?

JOB SEEKER: I'm afraid I can't. I can drive a car, but I can't drive a bus.

AGENCY OWNER: That's too bad. Let's keep looking here. Hmm. Here's one. The Renaissance Restaurant is looking for a chef. Can you cook?

JOB SEEKER: Oh, no! I can't cook at all!

AGENCY OWNER: Well, here's a job for a secretary. Can you type?

JOB SEEKER: No, I can't.

AGENCY OWNER: Hmm. This school is looking for a teacher. Can you teach?

JOB SEEKER: Sorry. I can't.

AGENCY OWNER: Here's one for a painter.

JOB SEEKER: No, definitely not. I can't paint.

AGENCY OWNER: This company is looking for a truck driver.

JOB SEEKER: I can't drive a truck.

AGENCY OWNER: This place needs a dancer.

JOB SEEKER: I can't dance.

AGENCY OWNER: Here's one for a writer.

JOB SEEKER: I can't write. This is terrible! I can't believe this! I can't bake, I can't drive a bus, I can't cook, I can't type, I can't teach, I can't paint, I can't drive a truck, I can't dance, I can't write. I can't do ANYTHING!! Woe is me! What can I do?! What can I do? What can I do?

AGENCY OWNER: You can act!

JOB SEEKER: I can what?

AGENCY OWNER: You can act! And I have a job for you! Here! The Stagelight Theater Company is looking for an actor.

JOB SEEKER: Me? An actor?

AGENCY OWNER: Yes. You're an excellent actor. Go down to the Stagelight Theater right now. I think you can get the job.

JOB SEEKER: Do you really think so?

AGENCY OWNER: Believe me, you can act. You're a terrific actor.

JOB SEEKER: Thank you. Thank you so much.

GRAMMAR

Can

Can	I he she it we you they	sing?

I He She It We You They	can can't	dance.

Yes,	I he she it we you they	can.

No,	I he she it we you they	can't.

FUNCTIONS

Inquiring about Ability

Can you *speak Hungarian?*

Expressing Ability

Yes, I can.
I can *speak Japanese.*

Of course *he* can.

Expressing Inability

I can't *type.*
No, I can't.

Asking for and Reporting Information

He *fixes cars every day.*
He's a *mechanic.*

Tell me, _____.

Inquiring about Want–Desire

What kind of *job* are you looking for?

Complimenting

Very nice!
That's beautiful!
You're a terrific *actor.*

Hesitating

Hmm.
Well, . . .

Expressing Regret

That's too bad.

Sorry.
I'm sorry.

SEGMENT 21

- Obligations
- Invitations
- Have to
- Can

"I'm sorry I can't go with you. I have some things I have to do . . . Side by Side."

LESSON MENU

SBS-TV Backstage Bulletin Board

TO: Production Crew
Sets and props for this segment:

Living Room
sofa
coffee table
refreshments
balloons

Street
buses
cars
briefcases

Office
desks
desk calendar
telephone
computer

TO: Cast Members
Key words in this segment:

do laundry	ballgame
go bowling	dentist
go sailing	doctor
go shopping	party
catch a plane	tickets
catch a train	depressed
chat	sorry
make a call	tomorrow evening
stop	tonight

I	you	can	clean	doctor
I'm	your	can't	do	party
me	they	has	go	to
my	their	have	work	

Herbert is depressed. He's having a party today, but his friends <u>can't go</u>[1] to his party. They're all busy.

A. _____[2] you go to Herbert's party?

B. No, _____ _____[3]. I have

to _____[4].

A. Can you _____[5] to Herbert's party?

B. No, we can't. We _____

_____ _____[6] our house.

A. Well, _____ _____[7] children

_____[8] to Herbert's party?

B. No, _____ _____[9]. They

have to _____[10] _____[11] homework.

A. Can you go to Herbert's _____[12]?

B. Yes, I _____[13].

C. No, _____[14] can't. You 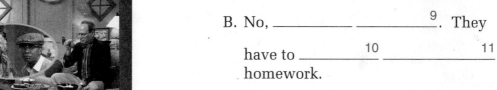 _____ _____ _____[15] to the dentist.

She _____[16]. She _____ _____ _____[17] to the dentist.

B. That's right. I _____[18].

A. Can Michael _____ _____ [19] Herbert's party?

B. No, he can't. He _____ _____ [20] go _____ [21] the _____ [22].

A. Herbert?

B. Yes?

A. _____ [23] sorry, Herbert. Your friends _____ [24] come to your party. They all have things they _____ _____ _____ [25].

B. Oh. Well, _____ _____ [26] come to _____ [27] party?

A. _____ [28]? Oh, no. I'm afraid _____ _____ [29]. I _____ _____ [30] stay here and _____ [31]. Sorry.

B. That's okay. _____ [32] understand.

(**ON CAMERA**)

Herbert is inviting you and your family to his party, but you're all busy.

HERBERT: Can you come to my party?

YOU: No, I can't. I have to ....

HERBERT: Can your .... come to my party?

YOU: I'm sorry. (He/She/They) can't. (He/She/They) (has to/have to) ....

....

HERBERT: Well, can your .... come to my party?

YOU: I'm afraid (he/she/they) can't. (He/She/They) (has to/have to) ....

....

HERBERT: That's okay. I understand.

21.2 I'M SORRY. I CAN'T. (34:34)

INFORMATION CHECK

Watch the scene and then put a check (✔) next to the things Steve HAS TO do.

_____ work late	_____ go to a ballgame
_____ do laundry	_____ go to a party
_____ go bowling	_____ have dinner with Julie
_____ go sailing	_____ have dinner with Mom and Dad
✔ go shopping	_____ clean his apartment

EDITING MIX-UP 1

The video editor made a mistake! Put Steve's conversation with Bob in the correct order.

_____ Tonight? Let me see. Gee, no, I can't.
I have to go shopping.

_____ Fine, Bob.

_____ Oh. That's too bad.

<u>1</u> Oh hi, Steve!   How are you today?

_____ But thanks for asking me.

_____ Hey, Steve, can you go to the ballgame with me tonight? I have two tickets.

_____ Sure.

EDITING MIX-UP 2

Put Steve's conversation with Patty in the correct order.

_____ Sorry you can't come.

_____ Great. Listen, Steve, my roommate and I are
having a party tomorrow evening. Can you come?

_____ See you later.

_____ Oh hi, Patty! How are you doing?

_____ Me, too.

<u>1</u> Hi, Steve!

_____ Tomorrow evening? Let me check. Hmm. Looks like I can't.
I have to do my laundry. But thanks for inviting me.

EDITING MIX-UP 3

Put Steve's conversation with Alan in the correct order.

_____ This Saturday? Hmm. I don't know. Nope. I'm afraid not. I have to clean my apartment this Saturday.

__1__ Hi, Alan. How are you doing today?

_____ See you later, Alan.

_____ Yes, I do. I really have to clean it this Saturday.

_____ Do you have to clean it on Saturday?

_____ Well, all right, Steve. See you later.

_____ Pretty good. Listen, Steve, can you go sailing this Saturday?

WHAT'S JULIE SAYING?

Listen to Steve's conversation with Julie. Can you guess what she's saying? Circle the best answer.

1 Hi, Julie. This is Steve.

  a. Hi, Steve. I'm calling from Miami.

  b. Hi, Steve. What are you doing?

  (c.) Hi, Steve. How are you doing?

2 Listen, Julie, can you have dinner with me on Sunday?

  a. On Sunday? Let me see. Of course, I can.

  b. On Sunday? Gee, I'm sorry. I can't.

  c. On Sunday? I see.

3 You can't?

  a. I'm afraid not. I have to fix my TV.

  b. I'm sorry. I can't. I have to eat dinner.

  c. Me, too.

4 You have to WHAT?

  a. Because it's broken.

  b. I have to fix my TV.

  c. I have a color TV.

5 Do you have to do that on Sunday?

  a. Yes, I do.

  b. Yes, I can.

  c. Yes, I have.

6 I see. Well, that's too bad. Maybe some other time.

  a. I'm sorry to hear that.

  b. Thanks for asking me.

  c. See you on Sunday.

What do you think Fred is saying to Steve? Fill in Fred's "missing lines" and then practice the conversation with a friend.

STEVE: Hi, Fred. This is Steve.

FRED: ....

STEVE: Great. Great. Listen, Fred, can you go bowling with me on Sunday?

FRED: ....

STEVE: That's too bad. I'm sorry you can't. And you have to do that on Sunday?

FRED: ....

STEVE: Of course I understand. You have to do what you have to do.

FRED: ....

STEVE: Sure. No problem.

FRED: ....

STEVE: Good-bye.

WHAT ARE MOM AND DAD SAYING?

How about Steve's parents? What do you think they're saying to him? Fill in their "missing lines" and then practice the conversation with a friend.

STEVE: Hi, Mom and Dad! This is Steve.

MOM AND DAD: ....

STEVE: Yes, I'm fine.

MOM AND DAD: ....

STEVE: Listen, can I possibly come over for dinner on Sunday?

MOM AND DAD: ....

STEVE: WHAT do you have to do?

MOM AND DAD: ....

STEVE: Oh, I see.

21.3 WE CAN'T TALK NOW! (37:47)

> FINISH THE RAP!

| can't | have to | catch | talk | I | We | now | stop |

We _____¹ talk now.

We can't _____² now.

_____ _____³ talk now.

We can't talk _____⁴.

I can't talk now. I _____ _____⁵ go to work.

I _____ _____⁶ now. I have to catch a train.

I can't chat now. _____ _____ _____⁷ make a call.

I _____⁸ stop now. I have to _____⁹ a plane.

_____ _____¹⁰ talk now. _____ _____ _____¹¹ go to work.

We can't _____¹² now. We have to _____¹³ a train.

We can't chat _____¹⁴. _____¹⁵ have to make a call.

We _____¹⁶ stop now. We have to _____¹⁷ a plane.

We can't talk now.

> WRITE YOUR OWN RAP!

We can't .... now.

I can't .... now. I have to ....

I can't .... now. I have to ....

I can't .... now. I have to ....

I can't .... now. I have to ....

We can't .... now. We have to ....

We can't .... now. We have to ....

We can't .... now. We have to ....

We can't .... now. We have to ....

We can't .... now.

WRAP-UP

CAST PARTY

Linda can't come to the cast party. She wrote a note very quickly and made lots of mistakes. Can you find the mistakes and correct them?

Please Come to the Side By Side TV Cast Party

When: 7:00 P.M., Friday, December 15

Where: Side By Side TV Studio

Bring Family and Friends

R.S.V.P.

Dear Steve and Bill,

I'm
~~X~~ very sorry, but I afraid John and I cant to come to you're party at Friday. John have to visits his parents in New York, and I have to working late.

Thanks because inviting us.

Sincerely,

Linda

WRITE YOUR OWN LETTER!

A friend invites YOU to a party. Write a letter to say you're sorry, but you can't go.

Please Come to a Birthday Party

For ....

When: ....

Where: ....

R.S.V.P.

Dear ....,

....

....

....

....

....

Sincerely,

....

FINISH THE SCRIPT!

Complete the conversation and then practice it with a friend.

A. Can you go to the movies on ....?
   (day of week)

B. I'm sorry. I can't. I have to .... How about ....?
   (day of week)

A. ....? Let me see. No, I'm afraid I can't. I have to ....
   (day of week)

   .... How about ....?
   (day of week)

B. ....? Let me see.
   (day of week)

THE NEXT LINE

Circle the best response.

1 How are you doing?
   (a.) Fine.
   b. I'm cooking dinner.

2 Can you go shopping with me on Saturday?
   a. I'm afraid.
   b. I'm afraid not.

3 Sorry you can't come.
   a. Me, too.
   b. Yes, please.

4 See you later.
   a. Bye.
   b. Let me see.

5 Looks like I can't go to the movies with you this week.
   a. How about tomorrow evening?
   b. Maybe some other time.

6 I'm sorry I can't go to your party.
   a. That's okay. I understand.
   b. That's terrible.

WRONG LINE

Circle the expression that doesn't belong.

1 a. I'm sorry. I can't.   b. I'm afraid not.   (c.) Of course I can.   d. I'm afraid I can't.

2 a. Let me see.   b. Definitely.   c. I don't know.   d. Let me check.

3 a. That's okay.   b. I understand.   c. No problem.   d. That's terrible!

4 a. Fine.   b. Sick.   c. Great.   d. Pretty good.

5 a. Bye.   b. Hi.   c. See you later.   d. Have a nice day.

6 a. I'm sorry.   b. That's too bad.   c. Maybe some other time.   d. That's wonderful!

21.1 THEY CAN'T GO TO HERBERT'S PARTY (33:00)

INTERVIEWER: Herbert is depressed. He's having a party today, but his friends can't go to his party. They're all busy.

INTERVIEWER: Can you go to Herbert's party?
FRIEND 1: No, I can't. I have to work.

INTERVIEWER: Can you go to Herbert's party?
FRIEND 2: No, we can't. We have to clean our house.

INTERVIEWER: Well, can your children go to Herbert's party?
FRIEND 3: No, they can't. They have to do their homework.

INTERVIEWER: Can you go to Herbert's party?
FRIEND 4: Yes, I can.
FRIEND 5: No, you can't. You have to go to the dentist.
(To Interviewer.)
She can't. She has to go to the dentist.
FRIEND 4: That's right. I can't.

INTERVIEWER: Can Michael go to Herbert's party?
FRIEND 6: No, he can't. He has to go to the doctor.

INTERVIEWER: Herbert?
HERBERT: Yes?
INTERVIEWER: I'm sorry, Herbert. Your friends can't come to your party. They all have things they have to do.

HERBERT: Oh. Well, can YOU come to my party?
INTERVIEWER: Me? Oh, no. I'm afraid I can't. I have to stay here and work. Sorry.
HERBERT: That's okay. I understand.

21.2 I'M SORRY. I CAN'T. (34:34)

BOB: Oh hi, Steve! How are you today?
STEVE: Fine, Bob.
BOB: Hey, Steve, can you go to the ballgame with me tonight? I have two tickets.
STEVE: Tonight? Let me see. Gee, no, I can't. I have to go shopping.
BOB: Oh. That's too bad.
STEVE: But thanks for asking me.
BOB: Sure.

PATTY: Hi, Steve!
STEVE: Oh hi, Patty! How are you doing?
PATTY: Great. Listen, Steve, my roommate and I are having a party tomorrow evening. Can you come?
STEVE: Tomorrow evening? Let me check. Hmm. Looks like I can't. I have to do my laundry. But thanks for inviting me.
PATTY: Sorry you can't come.
STEVE: Me, too.
PATTY: See you later.
STEVE: See you later.

ALAN:	Steve!
STEVE:	Hi, Alan. How are you doing today?
ALAN:	Pretty good. Listen, Steve, can you go sailing this Saturday?
STEVE:	This Saturday? Hmm. I don't know. Nope. I'm afraid not. I have to clean my apartment this Saturday.
ALAN:	Do you have to clean it on Saturday?
STEVE:	Yes, I do. I really have to clean it this Saturday.
ALAN:	Well, all right, Steve. See you later.
STEVE:	See you later, Alan.

(Steve makes a telephone call.)

STEVE:	Hi, Julie. This is Steve. Listen, Julie, can you have dinner with me on Sunday? You can't? You have to WHAT? Do you have to do that on Sunday? I see. Well, that's too bad. Maybe some other time. Bye.

(Steve makes another telephone call.)

STEVE:	Hi, Fred. This is Steve. Great. Great. Listen, Fred, can you go bowling with me on Sunday? That's too bad. I'm sorry you can't. And you have to do that on Sunday? Of course I understand. You have to do what you have to do. Sure. No problem. Good-bye.

(Steve makes another telephone call.)

STEVE:	Hi, Mom and Dad! This is Steve. Yes, I'm fine. Listen, can I possibly come over for dinner on Sunday? WHAT do you have to do? Oh, I see.

**21.3 WE CAN'T TALK NOW!—
GrammarRap** (37:47)

We can't talk now.
We can't talk now.
We can't talk now.
We can't talk now.

I can't talk now.
I have to go to work.
  I can't stop now.
  I have to catch a train.

I can't chat now.
I have to make a call.
  I can't stop now.
  I have to catch a plane.

We can't talk now.
We have to go to work.
We can't stop now.
We have to catch a train.

We can't chat now.
We have to make a call.
We can't stop now.
We have to catch a plane.

We can't talk now.
We can't talk now.
We can't talk now.
We can't talk now.

GRAMMAR

Can

Can	I he she it we you they	go to the party?

I He She It We You They	can can't	go to the party.

Have to

I We You They	have to	work.
He She It	has to	

Yes,	I he she it we you they	can.

No,	I he she it we you they	can't.

FUNCTIONS

Inquiring about Ability

Can *Michael go to Herbert's party?*

Expressing Ability

Yes, *I* can.

Expressing Inability

No, *I* can't.

Expressing Obligation

I have to *do my laundry.*
He has to *go to the doctor.*

Extending an Invitation

Can you *go to the ballgame* with me *tonight?*

Declining an Invitation

Sorry.
I'm sorry. I can't.
I'm afraid I can't.
Gee! No, I can't.
Looks like I can't.

I'm afraid not.

Expressing Regret

Sorry.
I'm sorry *you can't come.*

That's too bad.

Maybe some other time.

Greeting People

Hi! How are you today?
Hi! How are you doing?

Hesitating

Hmm.

Let me see.
Let me check.

I don't know.

Indicating Understanding

I see.

That's okay. I understand.
Of course I understand.

Sure.

No problem.

SEGMENT 22

- **Plans and Intentions**
- **Future: Going to**

"We're gonna run, we're gonna walk, we're gonna sit, we're gonna talk . . . together Side by Side."

LESSON MENU

SBS-TV Backstage Bulletin Board

TO: Production Crew
Sets and props for this segment:

Dorm Room
bed
books
bookbag
ticket
clothes
headphones
stereo

Party
balloons
decorations
food
glasses

Bedroom
skirt
jacket
pajamas
suitcase
sunglasses
tie
toothbrush

Kitchen
wrench
sink

TO: Cast Members
Key words in this segment:

tomorrow morning/afternoon/evening/night
this week/month/year
next week/month/year

right now   at once   tomorrow
immediately   right away   today

SOUND CHECK

I'm	We're				
He's	You're	going to	fix	help	be
She's	They're		work	clean	
It's					

INTERVIEWER: Tell me, Alice, what are you going to do tomorrow?

ALICE: _____ I'm going to work _____¹ in the yard.

INTERVIEWER: What's Fred going to do tomorrow?

ALICE: _____² his car.

FRED: Yes. _____³ my car,

and _____⁴ in the yard.

INTERVIEWER: What's the weather going to be like?

FRED: _____⁵ beautiful.

INTERVIEWER: Tell me, what are you going to do tomorrow?

HUSBAND: _____⁶ our house.

INTERVIEWER: I see.

HUSBAND: Yes. _____⁷ the living room,

and _____⁸ the basement.

WIFE: No, Harry. _____⁹ the basement,

and _____¹⁰ the living room.

_____¹¹ the basement.

INTERVIEWER: How about your children? Are they _____¹² help?

HUSBAND: Oh, yes. _____¹³ the attic.

INTERVIEWER: Well, happy cleaning!

22.2 PLANS FOR THE DAY (39:38)

WHAT'S HAPPENING?

Complete these sentences.

_b_ **1** Today he's going to the   a. tonight.

____ **2** He's going there   b. library.

____ **3** He's going to his chemistry class   c. concert ticket.

____ **4** He almost forgot his   d. this morning.

____ **5** He's going to a concert   e. this afternoon.

____ **6** Then they're going out to   f. this evening.

____ **7** He looked in his wallet and he has his   g. eat.

____ **8** He's going to be tired   h. chemistry book.

EDITING MIX-UP

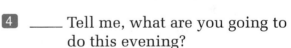

The video editor made a mistake! Put each pair of lines in the correct order.

1 ____ I'm going to the library.

_1_ What are you going to do today?

2 ____ Are you going to the library this morning?

____ Yes. I'm going there right now.

3 ____ My chemistry book? Oh, yes! Thanks for reminding me.

____ Don't forget your chemistry book over there.

4 ____ Tell me, what are you going to do this evening?

____ I'm going to a concert with some friends.

5 ____ Yes. Here it is.

____ Do you have your concert ticket?

6 ____ That's for sure.

____ You know, you're going to be tired tonight.

22.3 THEY'RE GOING TO THE BEACH (40:34)

WHAT'S HAPPENING?

1 Mr. and Mrs. Brown are going

to ____.

a. Washington D.C.

(b.) the beach

2 They're going there ____.

a. tomorrow morning

b. tomorrow afternoon

3 The reason is everybody else is

going ____.

a. tomorrow morning

b. tomorrow afternoon

4 They're going to a fancy restaurant

____.

a. tomorrow afternoon

b. tomorrow evening

5 They're going to a hotel ____.

a. tonight

b. tomorrow night

THE NEXT LINE

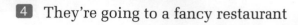

Circle the correct response to each line in the scene.

1 Don't forget your sunglasses!

(a.) They're right here.

b. There they are.

2 I'm going to wear this at the restaurant tomorrow evening. What do you think?

a. It's fine.

b. It's fun.

3 Do you like this jacket and tie?

a. It's purple.

b. It's perfect.

4 Don't forget your pajamas and toothbrush!

a. I have them right here.

b. Are they here?

5 Well, I think that's everything.

a. I don't know.

b. I think so.

6 We're going to have a great time at the beach tomorrow!

a. The weather's going to be beautiful!

b. It's going to be wonderful!

WHOSE LINE?

a "I'm going to wear this at the restaurant
tomorrow evening."

(Helen)   Howard

b "Do you like this jacket and tie?"

Helen   Howard

c "Don't forget your pajamas and toothbrush!"

Helen   Howard

d "I have them right here."

Helen   Howard

e "Well, I think that's everything."

Helen   Howard

PICTURE THIS!

Match the lines above with the following scenes from the video.

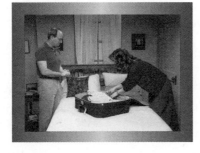

1 _a_

2 ____

3 ____

4 ____

5 ____

CLOSE-UP

You're on Side by Side TV! Tell the viewers: What are YOU going to do tomorrow morning?
tomorrow afternoon? tomorrow evening? tomorrow night?

....

....

....

....

22.4 WHEN ARE YOU GOING TO WASH YOUR CLOTHES? (41:47)

WHOSE LINE?

1	"When are you going to wash your clothes?"	Lance	Theodore
2	"Are you really going to wash them this week?"	Lance	Theodore
3	"Well, maybe next week."	Lance	Theodore
4	"Next week?! How about this week?"	Lance	Theodore
5	"There's no reason to get angry."	Lance	Theodore
6	"I promise."	Lance	Theodore
7	"This month?!"	Lance	Theodore
8	"I don't think you're going to wash them next month."	Lance	Theodore
9	"I'm going to wash your clothes!"	Lance	Theodore
10	"You're going to wash MY clothes?!"	Lance	Theodore
11	"You're NEVER going to wash them!"	Lance	Theodore
12	"Next year, I'm going to wash YOUR clothes!"	Lance	Theodore

EDITING MIX-UP

The video editor made a mistake! Put the following lines in the correct order.

_____ Lance, are you really going to wash them this week?

_____ Now come on, Theodore, calm down! There's no reason to get angry. I'm going to wash my clothes sometime this month. I promise.

__1__ Lance, when are you going to wash your clothes?

_____ Well, maybe next week.

_____ You're right! This IS a very busy month. I'm going to wash my clothes NEXT month. And that's a promise, Theodore.

_____ I'm going to wash them this week.

_____ Next week?! How about this week?

_____ Next month?! Lance, I don't believe you!

_____ This month?! Lance, I don't believe this! Are you serious?!

22.5 WHEN ARE YOU GOING TO CALL THE PLUMBER? (43:53)

EDITING MIX-UP

The video editor made a mistake! Put the following lines in the correct order.

_____ I'm fixing the sink.

_____ Sure I can!

_____ Yes!

_____ YOU'RE fixing the sink?!

__1__ Edward, what are you doing?

_____ Edward, come on! You can't fix the sink!

SOUND CHECK

| right away | right now | immediately | at once |

When are you going to call the plumber?

I'm going to call him

_____right now_____ 1.

Edward, I think we need a plumber

_____ 2.

_____ 3!!

You're right. I'm going to call the plumber

_____ 4!

CONTINUE THE SCENE!

Edward is calling the plumber. Complete their telephone conversation and practice it with a friend.

EDWARD: ....

PLUMBER: ....

EDWARD: ....

PLUMBER: ....

This person speaks very fast! Watch the scene several times and decide whether the following statements about his busy week are true or false.

Next Sunday:

1	He's going to visit his mother and father.	(True)	False
2	His mother is going to make soup.	True	False
3	His father is going to cook in the kitchen.	True	False
4	His parents are going to ask him about his job.	True	False
5	He's going to ask them about their friends.	True	False
6	They're going to have a good time.	True	False

SUNDAY

Next Monday:

7	He's going to go to work.	True	False
8	He's going to drive his car to work.	True	False
9	The mechanic is going to fix his car.	True	False
10	He's going to walk to work.	True	False
11	He's going to get his car after work.	True	False
12	It's going to be cheap to fix his car.	True	False
13	He's going to be upset.	True	False

MONDAY

Next Tuesday:

14	He's going to get to work late.	True	False
15	He's going to ask his boss for a raise.	True	False
16	His boss is going to give him a raise.	True	False
17	He isn't going to be happy.	True	False

TUESDAY

Next Wednesday:

18	He's going to fly to Chicago.	True	False
19	He's going to go to a museum in the morning.	True	False
20	He's going to have lunch alone.	True	False
21	He's going to a meeting in the afternoon.	True	False
22	He's going to drive home in the evening.	True	False
23	He's going to be very tired.	True	False

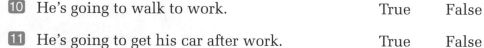

WEDNESDAY

Next Thursday:

24 He's going to write a report.   True   False

25 He's going to write about the lunch.   True   False

26 He's going to type the report and give it to his boss.   True   False

THURSDAY

Next Friday:

FRIDAY

27 He's going to go to the dentist before work.   True   False

28 The dentist is going to clean his teeth.   True   False

29 He's going to be nervous, but the dentist isn't going to hurt him.   True   False

30 He likes his dentist and he believes what his dentist says.   True   False

Next Saturday:

31 He's going to relax and have fun.   True   False

32 He's going to go bowling after he goes jogging.   True   False

33 He's going to have lunch at home.   True   False

34 He's going to go sailing in the afternoon.   True   False

35 Then he's going to go shopping.   True   False

36 He's going to see a play and go dancing in the evening.   True   False

SATURDAY

CLOSE-UP

You're on Side by Side TV! Write about YOUR busy week next week. Then tell a friend about your busy week as fast as you can!

I'm going to be very busy next week. It's going to be a very busy week. Do you want to know how busy I'm going to be? I'm going to tell you right now.

....

....

....

....

....

Yes, it's going to be a very busy week, but I guess I like it that way. Oh, I'm going to be late. I'm going to go now. Bye!

22.7 HAPPY NEW YEAR! (46:05)

1 ~~He's~~ (She's) going to start a new job in January.

2 He's / She's going to start a new job in February.

3 In March / April he's going to California to visit his brother / mother .

4 In March / April she's going there to visit her niece / sister .

5 She's / He's going to buy a new car in May.

6 She's / He's going to buy a new car in June.

7 He's / She's going to Canada in June / July .

8 She's going there in July / August .

She usually / always goes there then.

9 He's / She's going to acting school in September.

10 He's / She's going to acting school in October.

11 She's getting married in November / December .

12 He is / isn't going to get married in December.

SCENE REVIEW

Which of the months in this scene have these associations?

1 Months associated with school: _September, October_

2 Months associated with work: _____

3 Months associated with travel: _____

What do you think?

4 His favorite month is going to be .... because ....

5 Her favorite month is going to be .... because ....

PICTURE THIS!

Match these lines with the appropriate scenes below.

a. "Well, just two more minutes and it's a brand new year."

b. "Next year's going to be a great year!"

c. "I'm going to California in April to visit my sister."

d. "I'm going to buy a new car in May."

e. "You're going to WHAT?"

f. "Happy New Year!"

1   b

2   ____

3   ____

4   ____

5   ____

6   ____

CLOSE-UP

You're on Side by Side TV! Tell about your plans for next year.

I'm really looking forward to next year!

In January ....

In February ....

In March ....

In April ....

In May ....

In June ....

In July ....

In August ....

In September ....

In October ....

In November ....

In December ....

Next year is really going to be an exciting year!

WHAT'S THE QUESTION?

Bob is going away for the weekend. His friend Peter is asking him about his trip.

Who	What	When	Where	Why

1 _When are you going to_____ leave?   Tomorrow morning.

2 _____ stay?   At a small hotel.

3 _____ stay there?   Because I like small hotels.

4 _____ go with?   My cousins Tim and Philip.

5 _____ do there?   We're going to see the sights.

WHAT'S MY LINE?

1 Juan is ⟨going / go⟩ to visit his parents this weekend.

2 Noriko is going to ⟨have / has⟩ dinner with her friends this ⟨tonight / evening⟩.

3 Gary, ⟨is / are⟩ your roommate going to clean your apartment this ⟨weekend / night⟩?

4 When ⟨is / are⟩ you going to start your new job at the factory?

5 Gregory! Finish your homework right ⟨immediately / now⟩!

6 Our front door is broken. When ⟨are you going to / you are going to⟩ call the superintendent?

7 My brother and I are ⟨going to / going to go⟩ Mexico this year.

8 What ⟨are / am⟩ I going to cook for dinner tonight? We don't have any food in the refrigerator!

9 I'm going to call the police at ⟨away / once⟩!

10 You're ⟨going get / going to get⟩ married next month? Congratulations!

98   ••••• SEGMENT 22

22.1 SBS-TV ON LOCATION (38:44)

INTERVIEWER:	Hi, folks!
HUSBAND 1:	Oh hello.
WIFE 1:	Hi.
INTERVIEWER:	What are your names?
WIFE 1:	I'm Alice, and he's Fred.
INTERVIEWER:	Tell me, Alice, what are you going to do tomorrow?
WIFE 1:	I'm going to work in the yard.
INTERVIEWER:	What's Fred going to do tomorrow?
WIFE 1:	He's going to fix his car.
HUSBAND 1:	Yes. I'm going to fix my car, and she's going to work in the yard.
INTERVIEWER:	What's the weather going to be like?
HUSBAND 1:	It's going to be beautiful.
INTERVIEWER:	Well, have a nice day!
WIFE 1:	Thanks.
HUSBAND 1:	You, too.
INTERVIEWER:	Hello.
HUSBAND 2:	Hi.
WIFE 2:	Hello.
INTERVIEWER:	Tell me, what are you going to do tomorrow?
HUSBAND 2:	We're going to clean our house.
INTERVIEWER:	I see.
HUSBAND 2:	Yes. I'm going to clean the living room, and she's going to clean the basement.
WIFE 2:	No, Harry. YOU'RE going to clean the basement, and I'M going to clean the living room. *(To Interviewer.)* HE'S going to clean the basement.
INTERVIEWER:	How about your children? Are they going to help?
HUSBAND 2:	Oh, yes. They're going to clean the attic.
INTERVIEWER:	Well, happy cleaning!
HUSBAND 2:	Thanks.
WIFE 2:	Bye.
HUSBAND 2:	Who IS that?
WIFE 2:	I don't know.

22.2 PLANS FOR THE DAY (39:38)

INTERVIEWER:	What are you going to do today?
STUDENT:	I'm going to the library.
INTERVIEWER:	Are you going to the library this morning?
STUDENT:	Yes. I'm going there right now.
INTERVIEWER:	What are you going to do this afternoon?
STUDENT:	I'm going to my chemistry class.
INTERVIEWER:	I see. Don't forget your chemistry book over there.
STUDENT:	My chemistry book? Oh, yes! Thanks for reminding me.
INTERVIEWER:	You're welcome. Tell me, what are you going to do this evening?
STUDENT:	I'm going to a concert with some friends, and then we're all going out for a late dinner.
INTERVIEWER:	Do you have your concert ticket?
STUDENT:	Yes. Here it is.
INTERVIEWER:	You know, you're going to be tired tonight.
STUDENT:	That's for sure.

INTERVIEWER: Well, have a nice day, and enjoy the concert!

STUDENT: Thanks.

22.3 THEY'RE GOING TO THE BEACH (40:34)

PERSON 1: What are Mr. and Mrs. Brown going to do tomorrow?

PERSON 2: They're going to the beach.

MRS. BROWN: Don't forget your sunglasses!

MR. BROWN: They're right here.

PERSON 1: Are they going to the beach tomorrow morning?

MR. BROWN: You know, Helen, everybody's going to the beach tomorrow morning.

MRS. BROWN: You're right, Howard. Let's go tomorrow afternoon.

PERSON 2: No, I don't think so. I think they're going to the beach tomorrow afternoon.

PERSON 1: What are they going to do tomorrow evening?

MRS. BROWN: I'm going to wear this at the restaurant tomorrow evening. What do you think?

MR. BROWN: It's fine. Do you like this jacket and tie?

MRS. BROWN: It's perfect.

PERSON 2: They're going to a fancy restaurant near the beach.

PERSON 1: Are they going back home tomorrow night?

MRS. BROWN: Don't forget your pajamas and toothbrush!

MR. BROWN: I have them right here.

PERSON 2: No. They're going to a hotel.

MR. BROWN: Well, I think that's everything.

MRS. BROWN: I think so.

MR. BROWN: We're going to have a great time at the beach tomorrow!

MRS. BROWN: It's going to be wonderful!

22.4 WHEN ARE YOU GOING TO WASH YOUR CLOTHES? (41:47)

THEODORE: Lance! Lance!

LANCE: Hey! What's going on?

THEODORE: Lance, when are you going to wash your clothes?

LANCE: I'm going to wash them this week.

THEODORE: Lance, are you really going to wash them this week?

LANCE: Well, maybe next week.

THEODORE: Next week?! How about this week?

LANCE: Now come on, Theodore, calm down! There's no reason to get angry. I'm going to wash my clothes sometime this month. I promise.

THEODORE: This month?! Lance, I don't believe this! Are you serious?!

LANCE: You're right! This IS a very busy month. I'm going to wash my clothes NEXT month. And that's a promise, Theodore.

THEODORE: Next month?! Lance, I don't believe you! I don't think you're going to wash them next month. In fact, I don't think you're going to wash them this year!

LANCE: Whoa! What are you doing?

THEODORE: What do you think I'm doing? I'm going to wash your clothes!

LANCE: You're going to wash MY clothes?!

THEODORE: Yes, I'm going to wash your clothes, because you're not going to wash them! I know it! You're NEVER going to wash them!

LANCE: Gee, Theodore, I don't know what to say.

THEODORE: Don't say anything.

LANCE: Tell you what, Theodore. I'm going to make you a promise. Next year I'm going to wash YOUR clothes!

THEODORE: You're going to what?!

LANCE: Next year, I'm going to wash YOUR clothes! And that's a promise.

THEODORE: Sure, Lance!

LANCE: It's a promise!

22.5 WHEN ARE YOU GOING TO CALL THE PLUMBER? (43:53)

WIFE: Edward, what are you doing?

HUSBAND: I'm fixing the sink.

WIFE: YOU'RE fixing the sink?!

HUSBAND: Yes!

WIFE: Edward, come on! You can't fix the sink!

HUSBAND: Sure I can!

WIFE: When are you going to call the plumber?

HUSBAND: I'm going to call him right now.

WIFE: Edward, I think we need a plumber immediately. At once!!

HUSBAND: You're right. I'm going to call the plumber right away!

22.6 I'M GONNA BE VERY BUSY! (44:29)

FAST TALKER: I'm gonna be very busy next week. It's gonna be a very busy week. Do you wanna know how busy I'm gonna be? I'm gonna tell you right now.

Next Sunday I'm gonna visit my mother and father. My mother's gonna make soup, and my father's gonna cook chicken on the barbecue. They're gonna ask me about my work. I'm gonna ask them about their friends. We're gonna have a very nice time.

Next Monday I'm gonna go to work. I'm not gonna drive my car to work because I'm gonna bring my car to the mechanic and he's gonna fix it. I'm gonna take the bus to work. After work I'm gonna take the bus to the garage and get my car. The mechanic's gonna give me my bill, and I'm gonna be upset because it's gonna cost a lot of money.

Next Tuesday I'm gonna get to work early because I'm gonna talk to my boss. I'm gonna ask my boss for a raise. She's gonna say "No, maybe next year" and I'm gonna say "Okay" and walk out and I'm gonna be sad.

Next Wednesday I'm gonna fly to Chicago. I'm gonna go to a meeting in the morning, I'm gonna have lunch with some people, and I'm gonna go to another meeting in the afternoon. I'm gonna fly home in the evening, and I'm gonna be very tired.

Next Thursday I'm gonna write a report about my meetings in Chicago. I'm not gonna write about the lunch because the lunch isn't gonna be very good. I'm gonna type the report on my computer, I'm gonna print it on my printer, and I'm gonna give it to my boss.

Next Friday I'm not gonna go to work right away. I'm gonna go to the dentist. My dentist is gonna look at my teeth, and his assistant's gonna clean them. I'm gonna be a little nervous, but my dentist is gonna tell me, "Don't worry. I'm not gonna hurt you. Everything's gonna be okay." And I'm gonna believe him because my dentist is a very nice person.

Next Saturday I'm gonna relax and have fun. I'm gonna go jogging. Then I'm gonna go bowling. I'm gonna have lunch at my favorite restaurant. Then in the afternoon, I'm gonna go sailing. Then I'm gonna go shopping. In the evening, I'm gonna go to a movie with some friends, and then we're gonna go dancing.

Yes, it's gonna be a very busy week, but I guess I like it that way. Oh, I'm gonna be late. I'm gonna go now. Bye!

22.7 HAPPY NEW YEAR! (46:05)

MAN: Well, just two more minutes and it's a brand new year.

WOMAN: Just two more minutes. How about that!

MAN: This sure is a great New Year's party.

WOMAN: It sure is. It's a very nice party.

BOTH: Are you looking forward to . . .

MAN: I'm sorry. Go ahead.

WOMAN: Are you looking forward to next year?

MAN: Yes, I am. How about you?

WOMAN: Me, too. Next year's going to be a great year! In January I'm going to start a new job.

MAN: That's interesting. I'm going to start a new job in February.

WOMAN: How about that!

MAN: In March I'm going to California to visit my brother.

WOMAN: Really? I'm going to California in April to visit my sister.

MAN: Well, how do you like that!

WOMAN: May is going to be an exciting month. I'm going to buy a new car in May.

MAN: What a coincidence! I'm going to buy a new car in June!

WOMAN: I can't believe it!

MAN: It's amazing!

WOMAN: Are you going to go on a summer vacation next year?

MAN: Yes. I'm going to Canada in July. Don't tell me you're going to Canada, too!

WOMAN: I sure am. I'm going to go there in August. I always go to Canada in August . . . every year.

MAN: September is going to be a very important month. In September I'm going to acting school.

WOMAN: No! You're kidding! I'm going to acting school in October!

MAN: That's incredible! So what's going to happen with you in November?

WOMAN: November? Well . . . uh . . . I'm going to get married in November.

MAN: You're going to WHAT?

WOMAN: I'm going to get married in November.

MAN: Oh.

WOMAN: I suppose you're going to get married in December, right?

MAN: December? Uh . . . no . . . I'm not going to get married in December.

WOMAN: Look at the time! It's twelve o'clock! Happy New Year!

EVERYONE: Happy New Year!

MAN: Happy New Year!

GRAMMAR

Future: Going to

What	am	I	going to do?
	is	he she it	
	are	we you they	

(I am)	I'm	going to read.
(He is)	He's	
(She is)	She's	
(It is)	It's	
(We are)	We're	
(You are)	You're	
(They are)	They're	

Time Expressions

| I'm going to wash my clothes | today. this morning. this afternoon. this evening. tonight. | tomorrow. tomorrow morning. tomorrow afternoon. tomorrow evening. tomorrow night. | right now. right away. immediately. at once. |

| I'm going to fix my car | this/next | week. month. year. spring. summer. fall (autumn). winter. | Sunday. Monday. Tuesday. Wednesday. Thursday. Friday. Saturday. | January. February. March. April. May. June. | July. August. September. October. November. December. |

FUNCTIONS

Inquiring about Intention

What are you going to do *tomorrow?*

When are you going to *wash your clothes?*

Expressing Intention

I'm going to *paint my kitchen.*

I'm going to *wash my clothes this week.*

Asking for Information

Tell me, _____ ?

Expressing Good Wishes

Have a nice *day!*
Enjoy the *concert!*

"What's the forecast? What's the weather?

Rain or shine, we'll be together . . . Side by Side."

LESSON MENU

SBS-TV Backstage Bulletin Board

SBS-TV

TO: Production Crew

Sets and props for this segment:

TV Studio
weather
map

Classroom
desks
map
books

Bathroom
mirror
sink
razor
shaving cream

Sports Stadium
tickets

Train Station
tickets
suitcase

Movie Theater
tickets

Living Room
TV
sofa

Stage
gold records

TO: Cast Members

Key words in this segment:

forecast
clear
drizzle
foggy
a quarter to
a quarter after
half past
midnight
noon
What time . . . ?

begin
leave
go swimming
hope
hurry
shave
wait
want
late

23.1 WORLD WEATHER FORECAST (48:49)

1 It's going to be sunny in Puerto Rico.	Yes	No
2 It's going to be clear in Venezuela.	Yes	No
3 It's going to rain in France.	Yes	No
4 It's just going to rain a little in Poland.	Yes	No
5 It's going to snow in Ukraine.	Yes	No
6 It's going to be cloudy in Morocco.	Yes	No
7 It isn't going to be clear in Portugal.	Yes	No
8 It isn't going to be cold in Saudi Arabia.	Yes	No
9 It's going to be warm in Thailand.	Yes	No
10 It's going to be cool in Korea.	Yes	No
11 Wear a light jacket in Lithuania.	Yes	No

A GOOD DAY FOR THE BEACH

Put a check (✔) next to the countries where the weather is going to be good for a day at the beach.

✔ Puerto Rico   ___ Poland   ___ Portugal   ___ Korea

___ Venezuela   ___ Ukraine   ___ Saudi Arabia   ___ Lithuania

___ France   ___ Morocco   ___ Thailand

WEATHER CHALLENGE!

Watch the weather forecast for these 19 countries several times. How many answers can you give?

1	Afghanistan:	(cool)	cold		11	Indonesia:	cool	hot
2	Australia:	rain	warm		12	Italy:	rain	snow
3	Bolivia:	hot	foggy		13	Japan:	clear	drizzle
4	Canada:	sunny	snow		14	Malaysia:	warm	hot
5	Chile:	cool	clear		15	Mexico:	raining	sunny
6	Colombia:	cloudy	sunny		16	Panama:	hot	foggy
7	Ecuador:	hot	drizzle		17	Peru:	rain	clear
8	El Salvador:	warm	cool		18	Taiwan:	cold	cool
9	Estonia:	cloudy	foggy		19	United States:	snow	showers
10	Guatemala:	warm	rain					

ON CAMERA

You're on Side by Side TV! Give tomorrow's weather forecast for places around the world.

Hello, everybody. Let's take a look at tomorrow's weather forecast around the world.

It's going to ....

....

....

....

....

....

....

And that's the World Weather Forecast.

I'm .... Have a
      (your name)
nice day.

23.2 WHAT'S THE FORECAST? (50:42)

EDITING MIX-UP

The video editor made a mistake! Put the following lines in the correct order.

_____ The radio says it's going to rain.

_____ What's the forecast?

__1__ What are you going to do tomorrow?

_____ I hope you're right. I REALLY want to go swimming.

_____ That's strange! According to the newspaper, it's going to be sunny.

_____ I don't know. I want to go swimming, but I think the weather is going to be bad.

23.3 SBS-TV ON LOCATION (51:06)

SOUND CHECK

it	time	what	can	have	eleven	forty-five
it's	o'clock	what's	do	tell	fifteen	thirty

A. Excuse me. __What__ ¹ time is _____²?

B. It's _____³ o'clock.

A. Pardon me. Do you _____⁴ the time?

B. Yes. _____⁵ eleven _____⁶.

A. _____⁷ the _____⁸?

B. It's eleven _____⁹.

A. Excuse me. _____ 10 you _____ 11 me the time?

B. Certainly. It's eleven _____ 12.

A. What time _____ 13 you _____ 14?

B. It's twelve _____ 15.

WHAT'S THE TIME?

The interviewer is asking some other people the time. Draw the correct time on the clocks.

1 A. Excuse me. What time is it?

B. It's two o'clock.

2 A. Excuse me. What's the time?

B. It's three thirty.

3 A. Can you please tell me the time?

B. Sure. It's four forty-five.

4 A. Pardon me. What time do you have?

B. It's five fifteen.

5 A. Excuse me. Do you have the time?

B. Yes. It's six o'clock.

6 A. What time do you have?

B. It's seven forty-five.

EDITING MIX-UP

The video editor made a mistake! Put the following lines in the correct order.

_____ Why? What time is it?

_____ It begins at eight o'clock.

_____ It's seven thirty! We have to leave right now!

_____ Please try to hurry! I don't want to be late for the movie.

__1__ What time does the movie begin?

_____ Oh, but I can't leave now. I'm shaving!

_____ Oooh!

_____ At eight o'clock? Oh, no! We're going to be late!

WHOSE LINE?

1	"Oh, no! We're going to be late!"	Husband	(Wife)
2	"Oh, but I can't leave now. I'm shaving!"	Husband	Wife
3	"It's seven thirty! We have to leave right now!"	Husband	Wife
4	"Please try to hurry! I don't want to be late for the movie."	Husband	Wife
5	"Why? What time is it?"	Husband	Wife
6	"Oooh!"	Husband	Wife

23.5 SBS-TV ON LOCATION (51:56)

> YES, NO, OR MAYBE?

1	The game begins at a quarter after two.	(Yes)	No	Maybe
2	The game begins at two fifty.	Yes	No	Maybe
3	It's a baseball game.	Yes	No	Maybe
4	The game begins at two fifteen.	Yes	No	Maybe
5	The train to New York is Amtrak Train #64.	Yes	No	Maybe
6	The train to New York is in the station.	Yes	No	Maybe
7	The train to New York leaves at five thirty.	Yes	No	Maybe
8	The train to New York leaves at half past five.	Yes	No	Maybe
9	*The Flowers in Priscilla's Garden* is a movie.	Yes	No	Maybe
10	*The Flowers in Priscilla's Garden* begins at a quarter to eight.	Yes	No	Maybe
11	*The Flowers in Priscilla's Garden* starts at seven forty-five.	Yes	No	Maybe
12	*Space Wars* begins at a quarter after eight.	Yes	No	Maybe
13	Everybody is buying tickets for *The Flowers in Priscilla's Garden*.	Yes	No	Maybe

CONTINUE THE SCENE AT THE TRAIN STATION!

More people at the train station need information. Using the schedule below, ask and answer questions about the different trains.

Train Number	Destination	Leaves
54	New York	5:30
63	Chicago	6:15
72	Philadelphia	7:30
84	Miami	8:45
90	Cleveland	9:15
95	Los Angeles	10:45

A. What time does the train to

.... leave?

B. It leaves at (a quarter after/a quarter

to/half past) ....

A. (A quarter after/A quarter to/Half past)

....? Thanks.

CONTINUE THE SCENE AT THE MOVIE THEATER!

More people at the movie theater need information. Using the schedule below, ask and answer questions about the different movies.

Movies

THE FLOWERS IN PRISCILLA'S GARDEN	**7:45**
SPACE WARS	**8:15**
A HUNDRED BALLOONS	**8:30**
MURDER AT MIDNIGHT	**9:45**
THE LAST GOOD-BYE	**10:30**

A. What time does ....

.... start?

B. It begins at ....

A. ....? Thanks.
          (time)

23.6 IT'S TIME FOR BED   (52:43)

EDITING MIX-UP

The video editor made a mistake! Put the following lines in the correct order.

_____ Twelve noon?

_____ Yes, dear. It's time for bed.

_____ Twelve midnight?!

__1_ What time is it?

_____ No, don't be silly! It's nighttime.
         It's twelve midnight!

_____ It's twelve o'clock, dear.

_____ Oh.

23.7 TO BE WITH YOU (53:22)

FINISH THE SONG!

I'm	be	after	day	fall	right	April
it's	wait	in	month	summer		December
you	waiting	past	week			February
		to	year			July
		with				September

Any day, any ___week___ [1], any month, any _____ [2],

I'm gonna _____ [3] right here to be with you.

_____ [4] the spring, in the _____ [5],

in the winter, or the _____ [6]. Just call.

I'm _____ [7] here to be with you.

_____ [8] gonna wait from January, _____ [9], March,

_____ [10], May, June and _____ [11], August, _____ [12], October

and November, and all of _____ [13]. I'm going to wait . . .

_____ [14] one o' clock, a quarter _____ [15]. It's half _____ [16] one, a quarter

_____ [17] two. And I'm gonna _____ [18] right here to be with you.

Any _____ [19], any week, any _____ [20], any year,

I'm gonna wait _____ [21] here to be _____ [22] you.

Yes, I'm gonna wait right here _____ _____ [23] with _____ [24].

WHAT'S NEXT?

The rock singer is composing a new song. Can you help?

1 "I think of you in January, February, and ___March___."

2 "I'm yours in May, June, and _____."

3 "I want to be with you in the morning, afternoon, and _____."

4 "I need you every Monday, Tuesday, and _____."

5 "I love you in the summer, fall, and _____."

WHAT ARE THEY SAYING?

do	begin	it	a quarter after	eight	midnight	at
does	begins	it's	a quarter to	three		time
is	leaves		half past	two		what
				twelve		

1 A. ___What___ time ___does___ the train to Chicago leave?

B. It ___leaves___ at ___half___ ___past___ ___three___.

3 A. _____ _____ _____ the movie begin?

B. It _____ at _____ _____ _____ _____.

5 A. _____ you have the time?

B. Yes. _____ _____ _____ _____ _____.

2 A. Excuse me. What time _____ _____?

B. It's _____ _____ _____ _____.

4 A. What's the _____?

B. It's _____ o'clock, _____. Time for bed, dear.

6 A. _____ _____ does the ballgame _____?

B. _____ begins at _____ _____ _____.

23.1 WORLD WEATHER FORECAST
(48:49)

ANNOUNCER: Now here's the World Weather Forecast from Side by Side TV News, with Side by Side meteorologist, Maria Hernandez.

MARIA
HERNANDEZ: Hello, everybody. Let's take a look at tomorrow's weather forecast around the world.

It's going to be sunny in Puerto Rico. It's going to be cloudy in Venezuela. All our friends in France, get your umbrellas ready! It's going to rain. It isn't going to rain very hard in Poland. It's just going to drizzle. It's going to snow in Ukraine. It's going to be clear in Morocco. And be careful driving in Portugal. It's going to be foggy.

And looking at some temperatures around the world: It's going to be hot in Saudi Arabia. It's going to be warm in Thailand. Wear a light jacket in Korea. It's going to be cool. And put on a heavy coat in Lithuania. It's going to be cold! Now here's the weather forecast for other parts of the world. (Weather around the world.)

Afghanistan:	cool
Australia:	warm
Bolivia:	hot
Canada:	snow
Chile:	clear
Colombia:	sunny
Ecuador:	hot
El Salvador:	warm
Estonia:	foggy
Guatemala:	warm
Indonesia:	hot
Italy:	rain
Japan:	drizzle
Malaysia:	warm
Mexico:	sunny
Panama:	hot
Peru:	clear
Taiwan:	cool
United States:	snow

MARIA
HERNANDEZ: And that's the World Weather Forecast from Side by Side TV News. I'm Maria Hernandez. Have a nice day.

23.2 WHAT'S THE FORECAST? (50:42)

STUDENT 1: What are you going to do tomorrow?

STUDENT 2: I don't know. I want to go swimming, but I think the weather is going to be bad.

STUDENT 1: What's the forecast?

STUDENT 2: The radio says it's going to rain.

STUDENT 1: That's strange! According to the newspaper, it's going to be sunny.

STUDENT 2: I hope you're right. I REALLY want to go swimming.

23.3   SBS-TV ON LOCATION   (51:06)

INTERVIEWER: Excuse me. What time is it?

PERSON 1: It's eleven o'clock.

INTERVIEWER: Pardon me. Do you have the time?

PERSON 2: Yes. It's eleven fifteen.

INTERVIEWER: What's the time?

PERSON 3: It's eleven thirty.

INTERVIEWER: Excuse me. Can you tell me the time?

PERSON 4: Certainly. It's eleven forty-five.

INTERVIEWER: What time do you have?

PERSON 5: It's twelve o'clock.

23.4   WHAT TIME IS IT?   (51:31)

WIFE: What time does the movie begin?

HUSBAND: It begins at eight o'clock.

WIFE: At eight o'clock? Oh, no! We're going to be late!

HUSBAND: Why? What time is it?

WIFE: It's seven thirty! We have to leave right now!

HUSBAND: Oh, but I can't leave now. I'm shaving!

WIFE: Please try to hurry! I don't want to be late for the movie.

(The husband tries to hurry and cuts himself.)

HUSBAND: Oooh!

23.5   SBS-TV ON LOCATION   (51:56)

INTERVIEWER: Excuse me. What time does the game begin?

PERSON 1: It begins at a quarter after two.

INTERVIEWER: A quarter after two?

PERSON 1: Yes. That's right.

INTERVIEWER: Thanks.

ANNOUNCEMENT: This is the final boarding call for Amtrak Train number fifty-four to New York. Train number fifty-four. All aboard, please.

INTERVIEWER: Pardon me. Are you on the train to New York?

PERSON 2: Yes, I am.

INTERVIEWER: What time does the train leave?

PERSON 2: It leaves at half past five.

INTERVIEWER: Half past five? Thanks.

INTERVIEWER: Excuse me. What time does *The Flowers in Priscilla's Garden* start?

PERSON 3: *The Flowers in Priscilla's Garden?* I have no idea. I'm seeing *Space Wars.* Let me take a look. It begins at a quarter to eight.

INTERVIEWER: A quarter to eight? Thanks.

23.7 TO BE WITH YOU—Music Video (53:22)

Any day, any week,
Any month, any year,
I'm gonna wait right here
To be with you.

In the spring, in the summer,
In the winter, or the fall,
Just call. I'm waiting here
To be with you.

I'm gonna wait from
January, February,
March, April, May,
June and July,
August, September,
October and November,
And all of December.
I'm gonna wait . . .

It's one o'clock, a quarter after,
It's half past one, a quarter to two,
And I'm gonna wait right here
To be with you.

Any day, any week,
Any month, any year,
I'm gonna wait right here
To be with you.

Yes, I'm gonna wait right here
To be with you.

23.6 IT'S TIME FOR BED (52:43)

HUSBAND: What time is it?

WIFE: It's twelve o'clock, dear.

HUSBAND: Twelve noon?

WIFE: No, don't be silly! It's nighttime. It's twelve midnight!

HUSBAND: Twelve midnight?!

WIFE: Yes, dear. It's time for bed.

HUSBAND: Oh.

GRAMMAR

Future: Going to

What	am	I	**going to** do?
	is	he she it	
	are	we you they	

(I am)	I'm	**going to** read.
(He is)	He's	
(She is)	She's	
(It is)	It's	
(We are)	We're	
(You are)	You're	
(They are)	They're	

Time Expressions

It's	11:00 (eleven o'clock).
	11:15 (eleven fifteen/a quarter after eleven).
	11:30 (eleven thirty/half past eleven).
	11:45 (eleven forty-five/a quarter to twelve).
	noon.
	midnight.

Want to

I We You They	**want to**	study.
He She It	**wants to**	

FUNCTIONS

Inquiring about Intention

What are you going to do
tomorrow?

Expressing Want–Desire

I want to *go swimming.*
I really want to *go swimming.*

I hope *you're right.*

I don't want to *be late.*

Leave Taking

Have a nice day.

**Asking for and Reporting
Information**

What's the forecast?
    The radio says it's going to
    rain.
    According to the
    newspaper, it's going to
    be sunny.

What time is it?
What's the time?
What time do you have?
Do you have the time?

What time does the *train*
    leave?
    It leaves at *5:30.*

- "Aches and Pains"
- Past Tense: Regular and Irregular Verbs

"We cooked and cleaned and then we talked. We ate and drank and then we walked . . . Side by Side."

LESSON MENU

SBS-TV Backstage Bulletin Board

TO: Production Crew
Sets and props for this segment:

Office
clock
potato chips
coffee
popcorn
sandwich
soda

Living Room
coffee cups
sofa

TV Studio
paint roller
wrench
duster
mop

TO: Cast Members
Key words in this segment:

backache
earache
headache
stomachache
sore throat
toothache
cold

24.1 HOW DO YOU FEEL TODAY? (55:15)

EDITING MIX-UP

The video editor made a mistake! Put each set of lines in the correct order.

a
____ I feel great!

_1_ Hi, Bob. How are you today?

____ I'm glad to hear that.

b ____ I'm happy to hear that.

____ I feel fine.

____ Hello, Bob. How are you today?

c ____ Thanks.

____ Okay.

____ That's good. Have a nice lunch, Bob.

____ Hi, Bob. How are you doing today?

d ____ Thanks, Nancy.

____ So-so.

____ Hi, Bob. How are you doing?

____ Oh. Well, have a good afternoon, Bob.

e ____ Not so good.

____ Oh. I'm sorry to hear that.

____ Hi, Bob. How are you?

f ____ I feel terrible.

____ See you tomorrow, Alan.

____ Bob, you don't look very well. Are you okay?

____ I'm sorry to hear that. Well, see you tomorrow, Bob.

PICTURE THIS!

Match the conversations above with the following scenes.

1 _*c*_

2 ____

3 ____

4 ____

5 ____

6 ____

Circle the correct response to each line in the scene.

1 I feel fine.

   a. I'm sorry to hear that.

   (b.) I'm happy to hear that.

2 How are you doing?

   a. So-so.

   b. I'm eating.

3 See you tomorrow.

   a. Hi!

   b. See you tomorrow.

4 Are you okay?

   a. Yes. I'm fine.

   b. That's good.

5 I feel terrible.

   a. I'm sorry to hear that.

   b. I'm happy to hear that.

6 Have a nice lunch.

   a. Not so good.

   b. Thanks.

MATCH THE SENTENCES!

Match the sentences that have the same meaning.

  _d_ **1** I feel great!

  _____ **2** How are you?

  _____ **3** Hi!

  _____ **4** I'm glad to hear that.

a. Hello.

b. I'm happy to hear that.

c. How are you doing?

d. I feel fine.

FINISH THE SCRIPT!

Complete the following conversations and then practice them with a friend.

A. How are you doing?

B. ....

A. I'm happy to hear that.

A. How are you today?

B. ....

A. I'm sorry to hear that.

24.2 SBS-TV ON LOCATION (56:45)

PREVIEW

Help the cast rehearse important words in this segment.

backache	earache	sore throat	toothache
cold	headache	stomachache	

1 <u>headache</u>
2
3
4 _____

 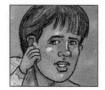 

5
6 _____
7

SOUND CHECK

What's the matter?

I have . . .

1 (a.) a headache
b. an earache

2 a. a backache
b. a stomachache

3 a. a headache
b. a toothache

4 a. a toothache
b. a backache

5 a. a headache
b. an earache

6 a. a sore throat
b. a toothache

7 a. a cold
b. a sore throat

122 ●●●●● SEGMENT 24

24.3 SBS-TV ON LOCATION (57:07)

SOUND CHECK

What did you do yesterday?

clean	cook	paint	plant	play	study	wait	wash	work

1 I _____worked_____.

2 I _____.

3 I _____ my windows.

4 I _____ cards with my friends.

5 I _____ my house.

6 I _____.

7 I _____ my bathroom.

8 I _____ flowers.

9 I _____ for the plumber all day.

24.4 WHAT'S THE MATTER? (57:28)

EDITING MIX-UP

The video editor made a mistake! Put the following lines in the correct order.

_____ Not so good.

_____ He has a backache.

__1__ How does David feel?

_____ He played basketball all day.

_____ Oh. I'm sorry to hear that.

_____ What's the matter?

_____ A backache? How did he get it?

FINISH THE SCRIPT!

These people don't feel well. Complete the following conversations and then practice them with a friend. In your conversations, use the words clean, paint, play, study, wait, wash, work.

A. How does Jennifer feel?

B. ....

A. What's the matter?

B. ....

A. ....? How did she get it?

B. .... all morning.

A. I'm sorry to hear that.

A. How does Frank feel?

B. ....

A. What's the matter?

B. ....

A. ....? How did he get it?

B. .... all afternoon.

A. I'm sorry to hear that.

A. How do you feel?

B. ....

A. What's the matter?

B. ....

A. ....? How did you get it?

B. .... all day.

A. I'm sorry to hear that.

SOUND CHECK

How do you feel today?

eat	sing
drink	sit

I have a ___stomachache___ [1].

I ___ate___ [2] cookies all afternoon.

I have a _____ [3].

I _____ [4] coffee all morning.

I have a terrible _____ [5].

I _____ [6] at my desk all day.

I have a very bad sore _____ [7].

I _____ [8] all day today.

THE NEXT LINE

Circle the correct response.

1 How do you feel?

  (a.) Not so good.

  b. Not really.

2 Are you feeling okay?

  a. Not so good.

  b. Not really.

3 How did you get it?

  a. I ate cookies all afternoon.

  b. Not so good.

4 I feel great!

  a. I'm glad to hear that.

  b. I'm sorry to hear that.

5 What did you do?

  a. Not so good.

  b. I sat at my desk all day today.

6 What's the matter?

  a. I have a headache.

  b. I played basketball.

7 I have a very bad sore throat.

  a. I'm sorry to hear that.

  b. How are you today?

8 Awful!

  a. What's the matter?

  b. How do you feel?

24.6 WE WORKED AT HOME ALL DAY (58:42)

clean	fix	paint	wash	floors	house	porch	sink

What did you do today?

I _____washed_____ ¹ my

_____ ².

Your _____ ³?

Yes! I _____ ⁴ my

_____ ⁵ all day!

What did you do today?

I _____ ⁶ my

_____ ⁷.

Your _____ ⁸?

Yes! I _____ ⁹ my

_____ ¹⁰ all day!

What did you do today?

I _____ ¹⁶ my

_____ ¹⁷.

Your _____ ¹⁸?

Yes! I _____ ¹⁹ my

_____ ²⁰ all day!

What did you do today?

I _____ ¹¹ my

_____ ¹².

Your _____ ¹³?

Yes! I _____ ¹⁴ my

_____ ¹⁵ all day!

I _____ ²¹ my floors.

I _____ ²² my house.

I _____ ²³ my porch.

I _____ ²⁴ my sink.

We worked at home all day!

WRITE YOUR OWN RAP!

What did YOU do today? Write a GrammarRap about yourself.

What did you do today?

I .... my ....

Your ....?

Yes! I .... my .... all day!

WHAT'S THE RIGHT WORD?

1 Susan ~~clean~~ (cleaned) her house yesterday. Today she has a terrible ~~toothache~~ backache.

2 When Tom is tired, he ~~watches~~ watched TV.

3 Last night Francine ~~eats~~ ate a lot. Today she has a very bad ~~headache~~ stomachache.

4 Anthony ~~played~~ play cards with his friends today. He ~~played~~ play cards yesterday, too.

5 Martha ~~waited~~ wait for her family to call her yesterday.

6 The president ~~talked~~ talks on television last night and everyone ~~listened~~ listen.

7 I ~~studied~~ study all day yesterday and I ~~studied~~ study all day today, too. I'm really tired!

8 When I ~~drink~~ drank a lot of coffee, I always get a bad ~~headache~~ backache.

9 What a busy day! We ~~cook~~ cooked and ~~cleaned~~ clean all morning!

10 I usually ~~exercise~~ exercised in the morning. Yesterday I ~~exercise~~ exercised in the afternoon.

WHAT DID THEY DO?

1 Mark doesn't usually play baseball, but he _____played_____ baseball all morning today.

2 Tanya never cleans her apartment, but she _____ it all day today.

3 I rarely eat ice cream, but I _____ ice cream yesterday afternoon.

4 Alice _____ her car yesterday. That's strange. She NEVER washes her car!

5 My children _____ dinner for me last night. My children don't usually cook dinner!

6 I have a backache. I _____ in a very uncomfortable chair all morning at work.

7 Of course you have a sore throat! You _____ all morning. I always get a sore throat when I sing.

8 I never drink coffee or tea, but I _____ a lot of coffee this weekend.

24.1 HOW DO YOU FEEL TODAY? (55:15)

(Bob is having a snack at the office.)

CO-WORKER 1: Hi, Bob. How are you today?
BOB: I feel great!
CO-WORKER 1: I'm glad to hear that.

(Bob is eating some more.)

CO-WORKER 2: Hello, Bob. How are you today?
BOB: I feel fine.
CO-WORKER 2: I'm happy to hear that.

(Bob is eating lunch.)

CO-WORKER 3: Hi, Bob. How are you doing today?
BOB: Okay.
CO-WORKER 3: That's good. Have a nice lunch, Bob.
BOB: Thanks.

(Bob is having an afternoon snack.)

CO-WORKER 4: Hi, Bob. How are you doing?
BOB: So-so.
CO-WORKER 4: Oh. Well, have a good afternoon, Bob.
BOB: Thanks, Nancy.

(Bob is still eating.)

CO-WORKER 5: Hi, Bob. How are you?
BOB: Not so good.
CO-WORKER 5: Oh. I'm sorry to hear that.

(Bob doesn't feel well.)

CO-WORKER 6: Bob, you don't look very well. Are you okay?
BOB: I feel terrible.
CO-WORKER 6: I'm sorry to hear that. Well, see you tomorrow, Bob.
BOB: See you tomorrow, Alan.

24.2 SBS-TV ON LOCATION (56:45)

INTERVIEWER: What's the matter?
PERSON 1: I have a headache.
PERSON 2: I have a stomachache.
PERSON 3: I have a toothache.
PERSON 4: I have a backache.
PERSON 5: I have an earache.
PERSON 6: I have a sore throat.
PERSON 7: I have a cold.

(Person 7 sneezes.)

Excuse me.
INTERVIEWER: Bless you.

24.3 SBS-TV ON LOCATION (57:07)

INTERVIEWER: What did you do yesterday?
PERSON 1: I worked.
PERSON 2: I cooked.
PERSON 3: I washed my windows.
PERSON 4: I played cards with my friends.
PERSON 5: I cleaned my house.
PERSON 6: I studied.
PERSON 7: I painted my bathroom.
PERSON 8: I planted flowers.
PERSON 9: I waited for the plumber all day.

24.4 WHAT'S THE MATTER? (57:28)

MOTHER: How does David feel?
DAUGHTER: Not so good.
MOTHER: What's the matter?
DAUGHTER: He has a backache.
MOTHER: A backache? How did he get it?
DAUGHTER: He played basketball all day.
MOTHER: Oh. I'm sorry to hear that.

24.5 SBS-TV ON LOCATION (57:47)

INTERVIEWER: How do you feel?
PERSON 1: Not so good.
INTERVIEWER: What's the matter?
PERSON 1: I have a stomachache.
INTERVIEWER: A stomachache? How did you get it?
PERSON 1: I ate cookies all afternoon.

INTERVIEWER: Are you feeling okay?
PERSON 2: Not really.
INTERVIEWER: What's the matter?
PERSON 2: I have a headache.
INTERVIEWER: A headache? That's too bad. How did you get it?
PERSON 2: I drank coffee all morning.

INTERVIEWER: How are you feeling?
PERSON 3: Not so great.

INTERVIEWER: What's wrong?
PERSON 3: I have a terrible backache.
INTERVIEWER: I'm sorry to hear that. What did you do?
PERSON 3: I sat at my desk all day today.

INTERVIEWER: How do you feel today?
PERSON 4: Awful!
INTERVIEWER: What's the matter?
PERSON 4: I have a very bad sore throat.
INTERVIEWER: I'm sorry to hear that. How did you get it?
PERSON 4: I sang all day today. And how do YOU feel today?
INTERVIEWER: I feel great!
PERSON 4: I'm glad to hear that.

24.6 WE WORKED AT HOME ALL DAY—GrammarRap (58:42)

What did you do today?
  I washed my floors.
Your floors?
  Yes! I washed my floors all day!

What did you do today?
  I cleaned my house.
Your house?
  Yes! I cleaned my house all day!

What did you do today?
  I painted my porch.
Your porch?
  Yes! I painted my porch all day!

What did you do today?
  I fixed my sink.
Your sink?
  Yes! I fixed my sink all day!

I washed my floors.
  I cleaned my house.
I painted my porch.
  I fixed my sink.
We worked at home all day!

GRAMMAR

Past Tense

I He She It We You They	worked yesterday.

[t]	I work**ed.** I danc**ed.**
[d]	I clean**ed** my house. I play**ed** baseball.
[ɪd]	I rest**ed.** I shout**ed.**

Irregular Verbs

eat – ate
drink – drank
sing – sang
sit – sat

FUNCTIONS

Asking for and Reporting Information

How do you feel today?
How are you?
  I feel *great/fine/okay.*
  So-so.
  Not so good.
  I feel terrible.
  I don't feel very well today.

What's the matter?
What seems to be the problem?
  I have *a headache.*
  I have *a* terrible *headache.*

What did you do yesterday?
  I *worked.*

How *did he get a backache?*

Responding to Information

I'm glad to hear that.
I'm sorry to hear that.
That's too bad.

Checking Understanding

A backache?

Greeting People

How are you today?
How are you doing today?

Leave Taking

Have a nice *lunch.*
Have a good *afternoon.*

See you tomorrow.

- **Past Activities**
- **Past Tense:**
  Questions
  Short Answers
  More Irregular Verbs

"They didn't do a lot today. They did a lot more yesterday . . . Side by Side."

LESSON MENU

SBS-TV Backstage Bulletin Board

SBS-TV

TO: Production Crew
Sets and props for this segment:

Kitchen
  table
  juice
  cereal
  counter
  groceries
  fish tank

TO: Cast Members
Key words in this segment:

fish	buy	clean
floor wax	brush	dirty
hair	go	white
paint	rest	yellow
pet food	smile	comfortable
poem	visit	uncomfortable
shampoo	work	beautiful
sofa	before	ugly
teeth	energetic	dull
toothpaste	tired	shiny
vitamins	happy	
weekend	sad	

SOUND CHECK

you	your	did	brush	sleep	hair
		didn't	brushed		

A. Good morning, Jessica.

B. Hi, Mom.

A. _____Did_____[1] you sleep well?

B. Yes, I _____[2].

A. Jessica?

B. Yes, Mom?

A. _____[3] you _____[4] your hair this morning?

B. Yes, I _____[5].

A. It looks very nice.

B. Thanks, Mom.

A. Good morning, Jimmy.

B. Hi, Mom.

A. _____[6] you _____[7] well last night?

B. No, I _____[8].

A. Oh. That's too bad. Jimmy?

B. Yes, Mom?

A. _____ _____ _____[9] your hair this morning?

B. No, I _____[10]. I _____[11] my teeth.

A. Well, please brush _____ _____[12] before you go to school. Okay, honey?

B. Okay, Mom.

WHAT DID THEY DO?

Saturday	Sunday
✔ work in my garden	

He _____worked in his garden_____ ¹
all weekend.

Saturday	Sunday
✔ visit some old friends from college	
✔ talk	

She _____
_____². ²

They _____ and
_____ and _____ ³
about the good old days.

Saturday	Sunday
✔ play baseball with my kids	✔ stay home and rest

On Saturday, she _____
_____⁴.

On Sunday, she _____
_____⁵ in her yard.

Saturday
✔ prepare for Leonard's visit
✔ dust the furniture
✔ vacuum the rugs
✔ clean all the bathrooms
✔ wash the windows
✔ cook
✔ bake

On Saturday, he and his wife _____
_____⁶.

They _____⁷.

They _____⁸.

They _____⁹.

They _____¹⁰.

They _____ ¹¹ a lot of food.

They _____ ¹² bread and
cookies and a big apple pie.

YES, NO, OR MAYBE?

1 Leonard and his family called on Sunday morning. (Yes) No Maybe

2 They said, "We can visit you today." Yes No Maybe

3 Leonard's children were sick. Yes No Maybe

4 They enjoyed their visit. Yes No Maybe

5 They didn't visit. Yes No Maybe

6 They wanted to visit, but they didn't feel well. Yes No Maybe

7 They're going to visit next month. Yes No Maybe

8 Leonard's cousin rested on Sunday and Sheila ate the apple pie. Yes No Maybe

CLOSE-UP

You're on Side by Side TV! Tell about your weekend.

1 Did you have a good weekend? ....

2 What did you do on Saturday? ....

....

3 What did you do on Sunday? ....

....

INTERVIEW

Interview two friends. What did they do on the weekend? Write their answers.

Name: ....   Name: ....

On Saturday, (he / she) ....   On Saturday (he / she) ....

....

On Sunday, (he / she) ....   On Sunday (he / she) ....

....

25.3 ON THE GO! (1:01:55)

Put a check (✔) next to the places where they went.

____ to the bank	____ to the doctor	____ to the library
____ bowling	____ to the drug store	____ to the post office
____ to the dentist	____ to the laundromat	✔ to the supermarket

SOUND CHECK

did	go	the	laundromat	bowling	to
didn't	went	this	library		

DAD: Hi, honey! Hi, Danny!

MOM: Hi, Bob!

DANNY: Hi, Dad!

MOM: What a busy day!

DAD: _____Did_____¹ you _____² to the bank this afternoon?

MOM: No, we _____³. We _____⁴ to the supermarket.

DAD: Oh, I see. Danny, _____⁵ you _____⁶ to the doctor _____⁷ morning?

DANNY: No, I _____⁸. I went _____ _____⁹ dentist.

DAD: Oh, that's right.

DANNY: Dad, did you _____ _____¹⁰ today?

DAD: No, I didn't. _____¹¹ morning I _____¹² to the post office, then I _____¹³ to the drug store, then I went _____ _____ _____¹⁴, and this afternoon I _____¹⁵ to the _____¹⁶.

DANNY: Boy, we sure are a busy family!

MOM: We're always on the _____¹⁷!

DANNY: I don't know where this day _____¹⁸!

YES, NO, OR MAYBE?

		Yes	No	Maybe
1	He got up late.	(Yes)	No	Maybe
2	He got up early.	Yes	No	Maybe
3	He got up at 6:00 in the morning.	Yes	No	Maybe
4	He got up at noon.	Yes	No	Maybe

5	She had a big breakfast.	Yes	No	Maybe
6	She didn't have any breakfast.	Yes	No	Maybe
7	She had coffee and bread for breakfast.	Yes	No	Maybe

8	He went to work today.	Yes	No	Maybe
9	He took the subway to work.	Yes	No	Maybe
10	He missed the bus.	Yes	No	Maybe

11	She didn't do her homework.	Yes	No	Maybe
12	She did her exercises.	Yes	No	Maybe
13	She rested all night.	Yes	No	Maybe

14	She went shopping today.	Yes	No	Maybe
15	She bought bananas.	Yes	No	Maybe
16	She bought oranges.	Yes	No	Maybe

17	She read the newspaper.	Yes	No	Maybe
18	She read a novel.	Yes	No	Maybe
19	She read a book.	Yes	No	Maybe

20	He wrote a letter to his son.	Yes	No	Maybe
21	He wrote a letter to his daughter.	Yes	No	Maybe
22	He wrote a poem.	Yes	No	Maybe

have	had	drank	left	missed	read
rested	took	watched	went	worked	wrote

•••••••••••••••••••••••••••• **Busy Day** ••••••••••••••••••••••••••••

I _____had_____ [1] a busy day today.

I _____ [2] and _____ [3] and _____ [4] all day.

I _____ [5] work late and _____ [6] the train.

I _____ [7] to walk home in the rain.

I didn't _____ [8] a thing to eat.

I _____ [9] the news and _____ [10] my feet.

I _____ [11] a bath,

And then I _____ [12].

I _____ [13] some milk,

And _____ [14] to bed.

WHAT'S MY LINE?

Did	buy	get up	have	take	write
	bought	got up	had	took	wrote

1 __Did__ you _____ the bus to school today?

No, I didn't. I _____ the subway.

2 _____ you _____ any milk at the supermarket?

I'm sorry. I didn't. But I _____ some juice.

3 _____ Jane _____ at 7:00 this morning?

No. She _____ late.

4 _____ you _____ a big dinner last night?

No. We _____ a small dinner. We didn't want to be late for the movie.

5 _____ you _____ to your grandmother?

Yes. I _____ her a very long letter.

25.5 PRESTO VITAMINS (1:04:01)

| bought | children | was | were | we're | tired | wife |

Before our family _____bought_____ [1] Presto Vitamins, we

_____ [2] always tired. I _____ [3] tired.

My _____ [4] was tired. My _____ [5] were

_____ [6], too. Now _____ [7] energetic,

because WE _____ [8] Presto Vitamins. How about you?

25.6 PRESTO PET FOOD (1:04:35)

The video editor made a mistake! Put the following lines in the correct order.

_____ My dog Homer was sad.

_____ All my fish were sad, too.

_____ Presto Dog Food for Homer.

_____ Presto Cat Food for Friskie.

_____ You know, before I bought Presto Pet Food, my pets were always sad.

_____ And Presto Fish Food for all my little friends right here!

__1__ Here, my little friends. It's dinnertime!

_____ My pets were all sad, but now they're happy, because I bought Presto Pet Food! How about you?

_____ Presto Pet Food. Available at pet stores and supemarkets everywhere.

_____ My cat Friskie was sad.

_____ Now my pets are happy, because I give them Presto Pet Food.

25.7 PRESTO PRODUCTS (1:05:28)

YES OR NO?

1	Her hair is always dirty.	Yes	(No)
2	Her hair is long.	Yes	No
3	Her hair isn't dirty now.	Yes	No

4	He never smiled.	Yes	No
5	He was embarrassed because his teeth were yellow.	Yes	No
6	He has a toothache.	Yes	No

7	Before she bought her Presto Sofa, she was never comfortable.	Yes	No
8	Her guests were uncomfortable.	Yes	No
9	Her guests never sit on her sofa.	Yes	No

10	He painted the rooms in his house.	Yes	No
11	He painted the outside of his house.	Yes	No
12	His house is ugly now.	Yes	No

13	His kitchen floor is really dull.	Yes	No
14	His kitchen floor was shiny before.	Yes	No
15	He drinks Presto Coffee.	Yes	No

EDITING MIX-UP 1

The video editor made a mistake! Put the following lines from the paint commercial in the correct order.

_____ It was ugly inside and outside.

_____ What a difference!

_____ My house looks beautiful now . . . thanks to Presto.

__1__ Before I bought Presto Paint, my house was ugly.

_____ But then I bought Presto Paint.

EDITING MIX-UP 2

The video editor made another mistake! Put the following lines from the floor wax commercial in the correct order.

_____ I mean, REALLY DULL.

_____ It's just beautiful.

_____ Then I bought Presto Floor Wax.

__1__ Let me tell you about my kitchen floor.

_____ Every morning, I sit in my kitchen, drink a cup of Presto Coffee, and say, "Thank you Presto Floor Wax. You changed my life!"

_____ It was dull.

_____ My kitchen floor is shiny now.

FIX THE COMMERCIALS!

1. My pets are happy because I feed them Presto ~~Floor Wax~~.   <u>Pet Food</u>

2. Now my teeth are white and I smile all the time thanks to Presto Paint.   _____

3. My hair is clean thanks to Presto Coffee.   _____

4. My house looks beautiful thanks to Presto Toothpaste.   _____

5. Let me tell you about my kitchen floor. It was dull. Then I bought Presto Shampoo.   _____

6. My guests are always comfortable when they sit on my Presto Vitamins.   _____

7. Before our family bought Presto Pet Food, we were always tired.   _____

WRITE YOUR OWN COMMERCIAL!

Before our family bought ...., we were always

                           (your product)

.... I was .... My (wife / husband)

was .... My children were ...., too. Now we're

.... because we bought ....

                                          (your product)

How about you?

BAD WEATHER

What a surprise! It rained yesterday in Centerville and everybody in town had to change their plans. Look at the calendars below and tell what everybody DID and DIDN'T do.

	Saturday
✗	go to the beach
✔	go to the movies

1 He didn't go to the beach.

He went to the movies.

	Saturday
✗	work in the yard
✔	write letters

2 _____

_____

	Saturday
✗	wash the car
✔	study English

3 _____

_____

	Saturday
✗	have a picnic
✔	eat at a restaurant

4 _____

_____

	Saturday
✗	walk to work
✔	take the bus

5 _____

_____

	Saturday
✗	paint the garage
✔	do my homework

6 _____

_____

	Saturday
✗	plant flowers
✔	read a novel

7 _____

_____

	Saturday
✗	play golf
✔	go bowling

8 _____

_____

TV CROSSWORD

Across →

1. Before I bought Presto Toothpaste, my
   _____ were yellow.
3. We _____ the bus to work this morning.
4. I was tired, but now I'm energetic because
   I take _____ every day.
6. Our teacher _____ sick yesterday.
7. This Presto Sofa is very _____.
8. I'm happy, and my dog is happy, _____.
9. Did you go to the bank _____ afternoon?
11. Can I wash my hair with your _____?
13. They _____ their furniture. Now it's clean.
15. What did you _____ this weekend?
16. Are you happy or _____?
17. I ate a big _____ this morning.

Down ↓

1. We went _____ the supermarket.
2. They visit us, and we visit _____.
3. I brush my teeth with _____.
4. Yesterday, I _____ an old friend.
5. I have two _____: a cat and a dog.
6. I _____ a poem. Do you want to hear it?
7. Our house was very dirty, so we _____ it.
10. She _____ on the sofa and watched TV.
12. I _____ a bad headache last night.
14. _____ you brush your hair this morning?
16. I always sit on the _____ when I'm in the
    living room.
17. He didn't _____ bananas. He bought
    apples.
18. We _____ a lot of food last night.

25.1   I BRUSHED MY TEETH (59:40)

MOTHER: Good morning, Jessica.
JESSICA: Hi, Mom.
MOTHER: Did you sleep well?
JESSICA: Yes, I did.
MOTHER: Jessica?
JESSICA: Yes, Mom?
MOTHER: Did you brush your hair this morning?
JESSICA: Yes, I did.
MOTHER: It looks very nice.
JESSICA: Thanks, Mom.
MOTHER: Good morning, Jimmy.
JIMMY: Hi, Mom.
MOTHER: Did you sleep well last night?
JIMMY: No, I didn't.
MOTHER: Oh. That's too bad. Jimmy?
JIMMY: Yes, Mom?
MOTHER: Did you brush your hair this morning?
JIMMY: No, I didn't. I brushed my teeth.
MOTHER: Well, please brush your hair before you go to school. Okay, honey?
JIMMY: Okay, Mom.

25.2   SBS-TV ON LOCATION (1:00:46)

INTERVIEWER: Did you have a nice weekend?
PERSON 1: Yes, I did. I worked in my garden all weekend.

INTERVIEWER: Did you have a good weekend?
PERSON 2: Yes. I visited some old friends from college and we just talked and talked and talked about the good old days.

INTERVIEWER: What did you do this weekend?
PERSON 3: On Saturday I played baseball with my kids, and on Sunday I stayed home and rested in my yard.

INTERVIEWER: Did you have a nice weekend?
PERSON 4: No, I didn't.
INTERVIEWER: I'm sorry to hear that. What happened?
PERSON 4: Well, my cousin Leonard called on Saturday morning. He and his wife and three kids wanted to visit us on Sunday. So all day Saturday, my wife Sheila and I prepared for their visit. We dusted the furniture, we vacuumed the rugs, we cleaned all the bathrooms, we washed the windows, we cooked a lot of food, and we baked bread and cookies and a big apple pie.
INTERVIEWER: You really worked hard. Did your cousin and his family enjoy their visit?
PERSON 4: What visit? They didn't come!
INTERVIEWER: They didn't?
PERSON 4: No. They called Sunday morning and said, "Sorry. We can't visit you today."
INTERVIEWER: That's terrible! Did they say why?
PERSON 4: No, they didn't.
INTERVIEWER: Well, I'm sorry to hear about your weekend.
PERSON 4: Thanks.

25.3   ON THE GO! (1:01:55)

DAD: Hi, honey! Hi, Danny!
MOM: Hi, Bob!
DANNY: Hi, Dad!
MOM: What a busy day!
DAD: Did you go to the bank this afternoon?

MOM:	No, we didn't. We went to the supermarket.
DAD:	Oh, I see. Danny, did you go to the doctor this morning?
DANNY:	No, I didn't. I went to the dentist.
DAD:	Oh, that's right.
DANNY:	Dad, did you go bowling today?
DAD:	No, I didn't. This morning I went to the post office, then I went to the drug store, then I went to the library, and this afternoon I went to the laundromat.
DANNY:	Boy, we sure are a busy family!
MOM:	We're always on the go!
DAD:	I don't know where this day went!

25.4 SBS-TV ON LOCATION (1:02:40)

INTERVIEWER:	Did you get up early today?
PERSON 1:	No, I didn't. I got up late.
INTERVIEWER:	Did you have a big breakfast today?
PERSON 2:	No, I didn't. I had a very small breakfast.
INTERVIEWER:	Did you take the bus to work this morning?
PERSON 3:	No, I didn't. I took the subway.
INTERVIEWER:	Did you do your homework last night?
PERSON 4:	No, I didn't. I did my exercises.

INTERVIEWER:	Did you buy apples today?
PERSON 5:	No, I didn't. I bought bananas. Do you want one?
INTERVIEWER:	No, thanks.
INTERVIEWER:	Did you read the newspaper today?
PERSON 6:	No, I didn't. I read a novel.
INTERVIEWER:	Did you write any letters today?
PERSON 7:	No, I didn't, but I wrote a poem.
INTERVIEWER:	A poem? Oh!
PERSON 7:	Do you want to hear it?
INTERVIEWER:	Hmm. I don't think we have time.
PERSON 7:	It's a short one.
INTERVIEWER:	Oh. Well, all right. Let's hear your poem.
PERSON 7:	It's called "Busy Day." I had a busy day today. I wrote and read and worked all day. I left work late and missed the train. I had to walk home in the rain. I didn't have a thing to eat. I watched the news and rested my feet. I took a bath, And then I read. I drank some milk And went to bed.
INTERVIEWER:	That's a very nice poem!
PERSON 7:	Thank you.
ANNOUNCER:	Side by Side TV will return after these commercial messages.

25.5 PRESTO VITAMINS (1:04:01)

HUSBAND:	Before our family bought Presto Vitamins, we were always tired. I was tired. My wife was tired. My children were tired, too. Now we're energetic, because WE bought

Presto Vitamins. How about you?

ANNOUNCER: Presto Vitamins. Available at drug stores and supermarkets everywhere.

25.6 PRESTO PET FOOD (1:04:35)

ELDERLY LADY: *(To her fish.)*
Here, my little friends. It's dinnertime!
(To the viewer.)
You know, before I bought Presto Pet Food, my pets were always sad. My dog Homer was sad. My cat Friskie was sad. All my fish were sad, too.

Now my pets are happy, because I give them Presto Pet Food. Presto Dog Food for Homer. Presto Cat Food for Friskie. And Presto Fish Food for all my little friends right here!

My pets were all sad, but now they're happy, because I bought Presto Pet Food! How about you?

ANNOUNCER: Presto Pet Food. Available at pet stores and supermarkets everywhere.

25.7 PRESTO PRODUCTS (1:05:28)

PERSON 1: Before I bought Presto Shampoo, my hair was always dirty. Now it's clean.

PERSON 2: Before I bought Presto Toothpaste, my teeth were always yellow. To tell the truth, I was very embarrassed. I never smiled. Now my teeth are white, and I smile all the time.

PERSON 3: Before I bought my Presto Sofa, I was always very uncomfortable when I sat in my living room, and I know my guests were uncomfortable, too. Now everybody's comfortable, thanks to my Presto Sofa!

PERSON 4: Before I bought Presto Paint, my house was ugly. It was ugly inside and outside. But then I bought Presto Paint. What a difference! My house looks beautiful now . . . thanks to Presto.

PERSON 5: Let me tell you about my kitchen floor. It was dull. I mean, REALLY DULL. Then I bought Presto Floor Wax. My kitchen floor is shiny now. It's just beautiful. Every morning, I sit in my kitchen, drink a cup of Presto Coffee, and say, "Thank you, Presto Floor Wax. You changed my life!"

ANNOUNCER: Consumers worldwide agree: If you aren't using Presto Products, you're living in the past. Presto . . . for the present!

GRAMMAR

Past Tense:
Yes/No Questions

Did	I he she it we you they	work?

Short Answers

Yes,	I he she it we you they	did.

No,	I he she it we you they	didn't.

Past Tense:
WH-Questions

What did	I he she it we you they	do?

To Be: Past Tense

I He She It	**was**	happy.
We You They	**were**	

Irregular Verbs

buy – bought
drink – drank
do – did
get – got
have – had
leave – left
read – read
take – took
write – wrote

Time Expressions

Did you study English	yesterday? yesterday morning? yesterday afternoon? yesterday evening? last night?

FUNCTIONS

Asking for and Reporting Information

Did you *go to the bank this afternoon?*
Yes, I did.
No I didn't.

You know, . . .

Let me tell you about *my kitchen floor.*

Complimenting

It looks very nice.

Greeting People

Hi.

SEGMENT 26

- **Past Activities**
- **To Be: Past Tense**

"I wasn't there. I didn't go. You didn't care. I didn't know.

But now we're . . . Side by Side."

LESSON MENU

26.1 WERE YOU AT THE BALLGAME LAST NIGHT? (1:07:00)
A young boy is upset because he thinks nobody in his family saw him play in a baseball game.

26.2 DID YOU . . .? (1:08:11)
Some people did. Some people didn't.

26.3 I REMEMBER (1:08:40)
An elderly couple reminisces about the time they were young.

SBS-TV Backstage Bulletin Board

TO: Production Crew
Sets and props for this segment:

Bedroom
  bed
  chair
  computer game

Kitchen
  table
  chairs
  cups
  plates
  orange juice
  pancakes
  cereal
  toast

Porch
  rocking chairs
  knitting needles
  newspaper

TO: Cast Members
Key words in this segment:

was	did
wasn't	didn't
were	
weren't	

26.1 WERE YOU AT THE BALLGAME LAST NIGHT? (1:07:00)

was	were	meeting	computer class	ballgame
		birthday party	movies	

1 Tommy's brother ___was___ at the _____ .

2 Tommy's father _____ at a _____ .

3 Tommy's mother _____ at her _____ .

4 Tommy's sisters _____ at a _____ .

5 Tommy's grandparents _____ at the _____ .

SOUND CHECK

was	wasn't	were	weren't

I can't believe it! Mom ___wasn't___ [1] there, Dad _____ [2]

there, my sisters _____ [3] there, my brother _____ [4]

there. Nobody _____ [5] at my ballgame.

That's not true, Tommy. Somebody _____ [6] at your

ballgame. Grandma and Grandpa _____ [7] there.

THE NEXT LINE

Circle the correct response.

1 Can I ask you a question?
   a. Morning, Tommy.
   (b.) Sure, Tommy.

2 Were you at the ballgame last night?
   a. Yes, they were.
   b. No, I wasn't.

3 I was at the movies.
   a. Where were you?
   b. Oh, I see.

4 Grandma and Grandpa were there.
   a. They were?
   b. How about Grandma and Grandpa?

5 They were?
   a. Yes, I was.
   b. Yes, they were.

6 Sorry I wasn't there.
   a. Oh, I see.
   b. That's okay.

26.2 DID YOU...? (1:08:11)

| did | didn't | was | wasn't | were | weren't |

A. _____Did_____ [1] you sleep well last night?

B. Yes, I _____ [2]. I _____ [3] tired.

A. _____ [4] Roger sleep well last night?

B. No, he _____ [5]. He _____ [6] tired.

A. _____ [7] you have a big breakfast today?

B. Yes, we _____ [8]. We _____ [9] very hungry.

A. _____ [10] Marcela and Carlos have a big breakfast today?

B. No, they _____ [11]. They _____ [12] hungry.

INTERVIEW

Interview two friends. Ask about things they did and write their answers in your reporter's notebook.

		Friend 1	**Friend 2**
1	Did you sleep well last night?	....	....
2	Did you have a big breakfast today?	....	....
3	Did you have a big dinner last night?	....	....
4	Did you ....?	....	....
5	Did you ....?	....	....

26.3 I REMEMBER (1:08:40)

Fill in the missing words and then, with a friend, role-play the scene with Gertrude and Harold.

was	were	did	go	eat	start	talk
wasn't	weren't	didn't	sit	have	rain	look

HAROLD: Gertrude?

GERTRUDE: Yes, Harold?

HAROLD: Do you remember when we _____*were*_____[1] young?

GERTRUDE: Of course I do. I remember like it _____[2] yesterday.

HAROLD: I remember the day we met. You _____[3] fourteen.

I _____[4] fifteen.

GERTRUDE: Actually, I _____[5] sixteen,

and you _____[6] seventeen.

HAROLD: I _____[7]?

GERTRUDE: Yes, you _____[8].

HAROLD: You _____[9] beautiful.

GERTRUDE: Oh no, I _____[10].

HAROLD: Yes, you _____[11], Gertrude. You _____[12] very beautiful.

GERTRUDE: You _____[13] handsome.

HAROLD: Me, handsome? No, I _____[14]. I _____[15] nothing special.

GERTRUDE: That's not true. You _____[16] very handsome, and very special. I

remember I _____[17] shy.

HAROLD: You _____[18] shy at all. You _____[19] very outgoing and very

popular.

GERTRUDE: Oh. That's right. I _____[20] very popular. And you _____[21]

very popular, too. You _____[22] always very busy.

HAROLD: I _____[23]. I _____[24] always with my friends.

GERTRUDE: Do you remember our first date?

HAROLD:	Of course. We _____ 25 to the zoo.

GERTRUDE:	No, we _____ 26. We _____ 27 to the park.

HAROLD:	We _____ 28 _____ 29 to the park, Gertrude. We

_____ 30 to the zoo. I remember.

GERTRUDE:	Harold, we _____ 31 to the park. We _____ 32 on a bench in

the park, and we _____ 33 for hours and hours.

HAROLD:	Gertrude, we _____ 34 _____ 35 to the park, and we

_____ 36 _____ 37 on a bench. We _____ 38 to the zoo

and _____ 39 at the animals

GERTRUDE:	You're wrong, Harold. I remember. I remember like it _____ 40

yesterday.

HAROLD:	You know what? The zoo _____ 41 in the park!

GERTRUDE:	That's right. It _____ 42. We _____ 43 to the zoo in the park.

HAROLD:	We _____ 44. And we _____ 45 on a bench, and we

_____ 46 for hours and hours.

GERTRUDE:	We _____ 47 some ice cream.

HAROLD:	That's right. And we _____ 48 some popcorn.

GERTRUDE:	That's right. We _____ 49.

HAROLD:	It _____ 50 a beautiful day.

GERTRUDE:	Actually, it _____ 51 to _____ 52.

HAROLD:	It _____ 53 _____ 54. It _____ 55 sunny!

GERTRUDE:	No, it _____ 56, Harold. It _____ 57 sunny. It _____ 58.

HAROLD:	It _____ 59 _____ 60, Gertrude.

GERTRUDE:	Yes, it _____ 61.

HAROLD:	Well, maybe you're right.

GERTRUDE:	It doesn't matter. It _____ 62 a very special day.

HAROLD:	You're right. It _____ 63. I remember it like it

_____ 64 yesterday.

WHAT'S THE RESPONSE?

Choose the best answer.

__j__ **1** Did you and your husband watch TV last night?

_____ **2** Was your brother late for class?

_____ **3** Did Mrs. Cummings go to the meeting at her son's school?

_____ **4** Did my brother call me last night?

_____ **5** Were you popular when you were a young boy?

_____ **6** Were you and your wife on time for the concert?

_____ **7** Was your sister at home yesterday?

_____ **8** Did your friends come to your baseball game?

_____ **9** Was I a quiet baby?

_____ **10** This food is delicious. Did you cook it?

a. No, you weren't.

b. No, they didn't.

c. Yes, we were.

d. Yes, I was.

e. No, I didn't.

f. No, he wasn't.

g. Yes, he did.

h. Yes, she did.

i. Yes, she was.

j. Yes, we did.

WHAT'S THE WORD?

was	wasn't	were	weren't	did	didn't

1 I _____was_____ tired today because I studied all night.

2 _____ you have a good time at the picnic?

3 We didn't eat a very large lunch because we _____ very hungry.

4 We met when we _____ eighteen years old.

5 It _____ a beautiful day yesterday. It _____ rain, and it _____ cloudy.

6 I'm sorry you _____ at the party. Everybody had a wonderful time.

7 I _____ sleep well last night because I _____ very upset.

8 Sally _____ late for work because she _____ at the train station on time.

9 I _____ do my exercises this morning because I _____ sick.

10 Where _____ you? We needed you! Why _____ you there? Why

_____ you call? We _____ all very concerned. _____ you okay, or

_____ there a problem?

MATCH THE LINES!

<u>f</u> **1** Fred didn't sleep very well because he ____.

____ **2** We had a big breakfast today because we ____.

____ **3** My boss was upset this morning because I ____.

____ **4** I drank all the juice because I ____.

____ **5** My children didn't eat a big dinner because they ____.

____ **6** Billy didn't finish his milk because he ____.

____ **7** I didn't miss the plane because I ____.

____ **8** I left the party early because I ____.

a. weren't hungry

b. was tired

c. wasn't late

d. were hungry

e. wasn't thirsty

f. wasn't tired

g. was thirsty

h. was late

SCRAMBLED SOUND TRACK

1 | meeting | father | . | at | Tommy's | was | a |

<u>Tommy's father was at a meeting.</u>

2 | your | you | class | Were | ? | computer | at |

_____

3 | rain | sunny | It | It | . | . | was | didn't |

_____

4 | ballgame | grandparents | the | at | . | were | Tommy's |

_____

5 | dinner | hungry | we | We | big | were | . | had | because | a |

_____

6 | the | the | at | zoo | went | looked | and | . | animals | to | They |

_____

7 | yesterday | very | work | to | . | I | I | because | go | was | didn't | sick |

_____

8 | ice cream | ate | eat | We | We | popcorn | . | . | didn't |

_____

9 | and | park | , | and | They | on | the | they | a | talked | bench | hours | . | in | for | hours | sat |

_____

26.1 WERE YOU AT THE BALLGAME LAST NIGHT? (1:07:00)

TOMMY: Hi, Jeff.

JEFF: Morning, Tommy.

TOMMY: Jeff, can I ask you a question?

JEFF: Sure, Tommy.

TOMMY: Were you at the ballgame last night?

JEFF: No, I wasn't. I was at the movies.

TOMMY: Oh, I see. Was DAD at my baseball game?

JEFF: No, he wasn't. He was at a meeting.

TOMMY: How about Mom? Was SHE there?

JEFF: No, Tommy, she wasn't. She was at her computer class.

TOMMY: How about Katie and Melissa? Were THEY at my game?

JEFF: No, they weren't. They were at Jennifer Henderson's birthday party.

TOMMY: I can't believe it! Mom wasn't there, Dad wasn't there, my sisters weren't there, my brother wasn't there. Nobody was at my ballgame.

JEFF: That's not true, Tommy.

TOMMY: Huh?

JEFF: Somebody WAS at your ballgame.

TOMMY: Who?

JEFF: Grandma and Grandpa were there.

TOMMY: They WERE?

JEFF: Yes, they were. And you know what they said?

TOMMY: No. What?

JEFF: You were terrific.

TOMMY: I was terrific?

JEFF: They said you were GREAT!

TOMMY: Yes!

JEFF: Hey, Tommy?

TOMMY: Yeah?

JEFF: Sorry I wasn't there.

TOMMY: That's okay. Next time.

26.2 DID YOU…? (1:08:11)

INTERVIEWER: Did you sleep well last night?

PERSON 1: Yes, I did. I was tired.

INTERVIEWER: Did Roger sleep well last night?

PERSON 2: No, he didn't. He wasn't tired.

INTERVIEWER: Did you have a big breakfast today?

PERSON 3: Yes, we did. We were very hungry.

INTERVIEWER: Did Marcela and Carlos have a big breakfast today?

PERSON 4: No, they didn't. They weren't hungry.

26.3   I REMEMBER   (1:08:40)

HAROLD: Gertrude?

GERTRUDE: Yes, Harold?

HAROLD: Do you remember when we were young?

GERTRUDE: Of course I do. I remember like it was yesterday.

HAROLD: I remember the day we met. You were fourteen. I was fifteen.

GERTRUDE: Actually, I was sixteen, and you were seventeen.

HAROLD: I was?

GERTRUDE: Yes, you were.

HAROLD: You were beautiful.

GERTRUDE: Oh no, I wasn't.

HAROLD: Yes, you were, Gertrude. You were very beautiful.

GERTRUDE   You were handsome.

HAROLD: Me, handsome? No, I wasn't. I was nothing special.

GERTRUDE: That's not true. You were very handsome, and very special. I remember I was shy.

HAROLD: You weren't shy at all. You were very outgoing and very popular.

GERTRUDE: Oh. That's right. I WAS very popular. And you were very popular, too. You were always very busy.

HAROLD: I was. I was always with my friends.

GERTRUDE: Do you remember our first date?

HAROLD: Of course. We went to the zoo.

GERTRUDE: No, we didn't. We went to the park.

HAROLD: We didn't go to the park, Gertrude. We went to the zoo. I remember.

GERTRUDE: Harold, we went to the park. We sat on a bench in the park, and we talked for hours and hours.

HAROLD: Gertrude, we didn't go to the park, and we didn't sit on a bench. We went to the zoo and looked at the animals.

GERTRUDE: You're wrong, Harold. I remember. I remember like it was yesterday.

HAROLD: You know what? The zoo was in the park!

GERTRUDE: That's right. It was. We went to the zoo in the park.

HAROLD: We did. And we sat on a bench, and we talked for hours and hours.

GERTRUDE: We ate some ice cream.

HAROLD: That's right. And we had some popcorn.

GERTRUDE: That's right. We did.

HAROLD: It was a beautiful day.

GERTRUDE: Actually, it started to rain.

HAROLD: It didn't rain. It was sunny!

GERTRUDE: No, it wasn't, Harold. It wasn't sunny. It rained.

HAROLD: It didn't rain, Gertrude.

GERTRUDE: Yes, it did.

HAROLD: Well, maybe you're right.

GERTRUDE: It doesn't matter. It was a very special day.

HAROLD: You're right. It was. I remember it like it was yesterday.

GRAMMAR

To Be: Past Tense

I He She It	was	happy.
We You They	were	

I He She It	wasn't	tired.
We You They	weren't	

Was	I he she it	late?
Were	we you they	

Yes,	I he she it	was.
	we you they	were.

No,	I he she it	wasn't.
	we you they	weren't.

FUNCTIONS

Asking for and Reporting Information

How about you?

Were you *at the ballgame last night?*
   No, I wasn't. I was *at the movies.*

Apologizing

Sorry *I wasn't there.*

Remembering

Do you remember *when we were young?*

Initiating a Topic

Can I ask you a question?

Attracting Someone's Attention

Gertrude?
Jeff, can I ask you a question?

Correcting

That's not true.

Actually, . . .

Agreeing

That's right.

It was.
We did.

Disagreeing

That's not true.

ANSWER KEY ●●

SEGMENT 14

Page 2

SOUND CHECK 1

1. a
2. b
3. a
4. a
5. a
6. b
7. a

Pages 2–3

SOUND CHECK 2

1. cook
2. cooks
3. does
4. cook
5. cooks
6. Does
7. cook
8. does
9. cook
10. does

Page 4

SOUND CHECK 3

1. Does
2. doesn't
3. does
4. cook
5. cooks
6. Does
7. cook
8. doesn't
9. does
10. cook
11. cooks

Page 5

SOUND CHECK

1. Do
2. go
3. do
4. like
5. Do
6. go
7. don't
8. don't like
9. do
10. like
11. like
12. do
13. go
14. don't
15. doesn't cook

Page 7

SCRAMBLED SOUND TRACK

1. Do you go to Stanley's Restaurant on Tuesday?
2. What kind of food do you like?
3. Stanley doesn't cook French food.
4. Does Stanley cook Chinese food on Friday?
5. I don't go to Stanley's Restaurant on Sunday because I don't like American food.

Page 8

EDITING MIX-UP

- 2
- 10
- 5
- 11
- 7
- 13
- 4
- 12
- 9
- 8
- 3
- 6
- 1

STANLEY'S FAVORITE CUSTOMERS

1. She goes to Stanley's Restaurant on Wednesday.

   She speaks Chinese, eats Chinese food, drinks Chinese wine, and listens to Chinese music.

2. He goes to Stanley's Restaurant on Saturday.

   He speaks Spanish, eats Mexican food, drinks Mexican wine, and listens to Mexican music.

3. They go to Stanley's Restaurant on Tuesday.

   They speak Greek, eat Greek food, drink Greek wine, and listen to Greek music.

Page 9

WHAT'S MY LINE?

1. like, likes
2. works, works
3. listen, listen
4. study, studies
5. go, goes
6. speak, speaks, speaks, speak
7. cooks, cooks, cooks

DO THEY OR DON'T THEY?

1. do
2. does
3. doesn't
4. do
5. does
6. don't
7. don't
8. do
9. doesn't
10. don't

SEGMENT 15

Pages 14–15

SCRIPT CHECK

1. d
2. e
3. b
4. f
5. a
6. c
7. b
8. c
9. a
10. b
11. e
12. a
13. d
14. c
15. e
16. c
17. a
18. b
19. d
20. b
21. e
22. f
23. c
24. d
25. a

Page 16

CAN YOU PREDICT?

1. a
2. a
3. b
4. b
5. a
6. b

SOUND CHECK

1. a
2. b
3. b
4. a
5. b
6. a

Page 17

VIDEO EDITOR

1. a, c
2. b, d
3. b, d

CAN YOU PREDICT?

1. b
2. b
3. a
4. b
5. a

WHAT'S MY LINE?

1. game shows
2. news programs

Page 18

CAN YOU PREDICT?

1. b
2. a
3. a
4. a
5. b

SOUND CHECK

1. b
2. a
3. b
4. b
5. b

Page 19

CAN YOU PREDICT?

1. b	4. b
2. a	5. b
3. a	6. a

Page 20

GUESTS AND HOST

1. b	3. b
2. a	4. b

EDITING MIX-UP 1

5
7
8
2
4
3
1
6

Page 21

WHAT'S THE LINE?

1. a	4. a
2. a	5. b
3. b	6. a

SOUND CHECK 1

1. music	11. jazz
2. like	12. does
3. kind	13. like
4. you	14. doesn't
5. what	15. likes
6. of	16. don't
7. like	17. do
8. your	18. she
9. do	19. does
10. like	20. I

Page 22

SOUND CHECK 2

1. sport	12. What's
2. do	13. your
3. you	14. Football
4. like	15. don't
5. which	16. like
6. does	17. do
7. like	18. LOVE
8. your	19. don't
9. is	20. do
10. Dave's	21. play
11. Baseball	22. Saturday

EDITING MIX-UP 2

2
8
5
7
1
3
6
4

Page 23

SCRAMBLED WORDS

1. favorite	7. classical music
2. comedies	
3. novels	8. adventure movies
4. golf	
5. poetry	9. performer
6. science fiction	10. cartoons
	11. short story

SEGMENT 16

Page 30

SOUND CHECK

1. you	6. us
2. me	7. it
3. him	8. you
4. her	9. her
5. them	10. me

Page 31

SOUND CHECK

1. b, d	6. always
2. b, c	7. usually
3. a, d	8. sometimes
4. a	9. rarely
5. b	10. never

Page 32

SCENE CHECK

1. is
2. rarely
3. usually

SOUND CHECK 1

1. never
2. sometimes
3. always

Pages 32–33

SOUND CHECK 2

1. wash	6. wash
2. washes	7. washes
3. do	8. do
4. washes	9. cleans
5. wash	10. cook

Page 33

SOUND CHECK 3

1. rarely	4. usually
2. never	5. never, always
3. sometimes	

Page 34

FINISH THE RAP!

1. always	7. usually
2. usually	8. sometimes
3. sometimes	9. rarely
4. never	10. never
5. never	11. never
6. always	

Page 35

SCRAMBLED WORDS

1. always	4. usually
2. rarely	5. never
3. sometimes	

WHAT'S MY LINE?

1. wash, washes	6. get, get
2. clean	7. sings, sing
3. studies	8. fixes, fix
4. watch, watches	9. washes, wash, wash
5. call, calls	

SEGMENT 17

Page 40

WHAT DO THEY HAVE?

1. a, c	5. a, b
2. a	6. b
3. a, b	7. b
4. b, c	

Page 41

SOUND EFFECTS MIX-UP

1. f	4. d
2. a	5. e
3. c	6. b

WHAT'S MY LINE?

1. Do, have I have	4. Does, have it has
2. Does, have she has	5. Do, have they have
3. Do, have we have	6. Does, have he has

Page 42

SOUND CHECK

1. has	15. have
2. brown	16. have
3. have	17. has
4. has	18. guitar
5. long	19. has
6. I'm	20. have
7. short	21. bicycle
8. don't	22. has
9. have	23. color
10. has	24. has
11. apartment	25. have
12. has	26. two
13. have	27. sisters
14. dog	28. friends

Page 43

WHICH SISTER?

1. brown	2. blue
3. short	4. long
5. short	6. tall
7. an apartment	8. a house
9. dog	10. cat
11. guitar	12. piano
13. bicycle	14. car
15. color	16. black-and-
17. just one	white
or two	18. a lot of

Page 44

TV CROSSWORD

See page 165.

SEGMENT 18

Page 48

SOUND CHECK

1. crying	4. cry
2. I'm crying	5. I'm
3. I	

SOUND CHECK

1. shivering	4. shiver
2. We're shivering	5. we're
3. We	

TELL ME WHY!

1. He's	8. sings
2. He	9. she's
3. blushes	10. They're
4. he's	11. they're
5. She's	12. They
6. she's	13. dance
7. She	14. they're

Page 49

SOUND CHECK

1. yawning	10. leave
2. yawning	11. shouting
3. yawning	12. shouting
4. I'm	13. I'm
5. I	14. I
6. yawn	15. shout
7. I'm	16. I'm
8. asking	17. leave
9. ask	18. leaving

Page 50

WHICH WORD?

1. nervous	7. hot
2. sad	8. hungry
3. happy	9. thirsty
4. tired	10. angry
5. sick	11. embarrassed
6. cold	

WHAT'S MY LINE?

1. hot	5. happy
2. hungry	6. thirsty
3. angry	7. nervous
4. cold	

Page 51

SCRAMBLED SOUND TRACK

a. When I'm nervous, I giggle.
b. When I'm angry, I shout.
c. When I'm happy, I smile.
d. When I'm nervous, I bite my nails.
e. I never get angry.
f. When I'm angry, my face turns red.
g. When I'm happy, I sing.
h. When I'm nervous, I perspire.
i. When I'm happy, I whistle.

MATCH THE LINES

1. d	4. b	7. i
2. h	5. f	8. c
3. a	6. e	9. g

Page 52

FINISH THE RAP!

1. smile	9. happy
2. frown	10. sad
3. blush	11. embarrassed
4. shout	12. mad
5. smiling	13. smile
6. frowning	14. frown
7. blushing	15. blush
8. shouting	16. shout

Page 53

WHAT'S MY LINE?

1. I'm	8. sleep
2. bite	9. I
3. smiling	10. cry
4. smile	11. giggling
5. turns	12. I'm
6. is turning	13. asking
7. I'm relaxing	14. ask

SEGMENT 19

Page 58

EDITING MIX-UP

3
5
1
6
7
4
2

SOUND CHECK

1. are	10. I'm
2. doing	11. washing
3. I'm	12. TODAY
4. washing	13. are
5. That's	14. doing
6. Do	15. is
7. wash	16. I'm
8. I	17. hear
9. wash	

Page 59

EDITING MIX-UP

5
7
1
10
8
3
11
2
4
9
6

WHAT'S THE LINE?

1. washing, wash
2. drinking, drink, drink
3. brushing, brush
4. feed, feeding

Page 61

FINISH THE RAP!

1. doing
2. working
3. late
4. doing
5. works
6. What's
7. He's
8. Cooking
9. he
10. that
11. He
12. cooks
13. on
14. doing
15. He's
16. his
17. Bathing
18. his
19. Why's
20. It's
21. always
22. his

Page 62

WRONG LINE

1. study
   studying
   at
   in
2. She
   Her
   dishes
3. usually
4. Are
   Does
   eats
   eating
5. watches
   watching
   today
6. shines
   shining
7. you
   your
8. they
   you

SCRAMBLED SOUND TRACK

1. He always cleans his apartment on Friday.
2. Do you usually wash the dishes in the bathtub?
3. She's walking to school because her bicycle is broken.
4. I never work late, but I'm working late today.
5. Does he usually cook spaghetti on Wednesday?
6. Why are you washing your dishes with "Ordinary Soap?"

SEGMENT 20

Page 66

SOUND CHECK

1. can
2. can't, can't
3. can
4. can't, can't

WHAT CAN THEY DO?

1. a
2. b
3. b
4. a
5. a
6. b

Page 67

SOUND CHECK

1. Can
2. can't
3. can

INFORMATION CHECK

1. b, c
2. a, c
3. b, c
4. c
5. a, c
6. b, c

Page 68

SCRAMBLED SOUND TRACK

A. Can Jack fix cars?
B. Of course he can. He fixes cars every day. He's a mechanic!

SCRIPT CHECK

1. baker
2. truck driver
3. teacher
4. chef
5. painter
6. writer
7. bus driver
8. dancer
9. secretary

Page 69

SCENE CHECK

1. can
2. can't
3. can
4. can't
5. can
6. can't
7. can't
8. can't
9. can't
10. can't
11. can't
12. can't
13. can

EDITING MIX-UP

1. 2 / 1
2. 2 / 1
3. 1 / 2
4. 2 / 1
5. 1 / 2
6. 2 / 1
7. 2 / 1
8. 2 / 1

Page 70

GOOD NEWS OR BAD NEWS?

1. Good news
2. Bad news
3. Good news
4. Good news
5. Bad news
6. Bad news
7. Good news
8. Bad news
9. Bad news
10. Good news
11. Good news

TO BE OR NOT TO BE AN ACTOR!

I can't bake, I can't drive a bus,
I can't cook, I can't type, I can't
teach, I can't paint, I can't drive a
truck, I can't dance, I can't write.

Page 71

CAN THEY OR CAN'T THEY?

1. can, secretary
2. can't
3. can, baker
4. teacher, can't
5. mechanic, can
6. truck driver, can
7. chef, can
8. painter, can't

SEGMENT 21

Pages 76–77

SOUND CHECK

1. can't go
2. Can
3. I can't
4. work
5. go
6. have to clean
7. can your
8. go
9. they can't
10. do
11. their
12. party
13. can
14. you
15. have to go
16. can't
17. has to go
18. can't
19. go to
20. has to
21. to
22. doctor
23. I'm
24. can't
25. have to do
26. can you
27. my
28. Me
29. I can't
30. have to
31. work
32. I

Page 78

INFORMATION CHECK

✔	___
___	___
✔	✔

EDITING MIX-UP 1

4
2
5
1
6
3
7

EDITING MIX-UP 2

5
3
7
2
6
1
4

Page 79

EDITING MIX-UP 3

3
1
7
5
4
6
2

WHAT'S JULIE SAYING?

1. c
2. b
3. a
4. b
5. a
6. b

Page 81

FINISH THE RAP!

1. can't
2. talk
3. We can't
4. now
5. have to
6. can't stop
7. I have to
8. can't
9. catch
10. We can't
11. We have to
12. stop
13. catch
14. now
15. We
16. can't
17. catch

Page 82

CAST PARTY

I'm   **I'm**
I̶ very sorry, but I̶ afraid John and I
can't   **your**   **on**
cant t̶o̶ come to you're party a̶t̶
      has   **visit**
Friday. John ha̶v̶e̶ to vis̶i̶ts his

parents in New York, and I have to
work
wo̶r̶king late.
      for
   Thanks bec̶a̶use inviting us.

Page 83

THE NEXT LINE

1. a
2. b
3. a
4. a
5. b
6. a

WRONG LINE

1. c
2. b
3. d
4. b
5. b
6. d

SEGMENT 22

Page 88

SOUND CHECK

1. I'm going to work
2. He's going to fix
3. I'm going to fix
4. she's going to work
5. It's going to be
6. We're going to clean
7. I'm going to clean
8. she's going to clean
9. You're going to clean
10. I'm going to clean
11. He's going to clean
12. going to
13. They're going to clean

Page 89

WHAT'S HAPPENING?

1. b
2. d
3. e
4. h
5. f
6. g
7. c
8. a

EDITING MIX-UP

1.	2
	1

4.	1
	2

2.	1
	2

5.	2
	1

3.	2
	1

6.	2
	1

Page 90

WHAT'S HAPPENING?

1. b
2. b
3. a
4. b
5. b

THE NEXT LINE

1. a
2. a
3. b
4. a
5. b
6. b

Page 91

WHOSE LINE?

a. Helen
b. Howard
c. Helen
d. Howard
e. Howard

PICTURE THIS!

1. a
2. c
3. b
4. e
5. d

Page 92

WHOSE LINE?

1. Theodore
2. Theodore
3. Lance
4. Theodore
5. Lance
6. Lance
7. Theodore
8. Theodore
9. Theodore
10. Lance
11. Theodore
12. Lance

EDITING MIX-UP

3
6
1
4
8
2
5
9
7

Page 93

EDITING MIX-UP

2
6
4
3
1
5

SOUND CHECK

1. right now
2. immediately
3. At once
4. right away

Pages 94–95

LISTENING CHALLENGE!

1. True
2. True
3. False
4. True
5. True
6. True
7. True
8. False
9. True
10. False
11. True
12. False
13. True
14. False
15. True
16. False
17. True
18. True
19. False
20. False
21. True
22. False
23. True
24. True
25. False
26. True
27. True
28. False
29. True
30. True
31. True
32. True
33. False
34. True
35. True
36. False

Page 96

SCENE CHECK

1. She's
2. He's
3. March, brother
4. April, sister
5. She's
6. He's
7. He's, July
8. August, always
9. He's
10. She's
11. November
12. isn't

SCENE REVIEW
1. September, October
2. January, February
3. March, April, July, August

Page 97

PICTURE THIS!
1. b
2. e
3. f
4. a
5. d
6. c

Page 98

WHAT'S THE QUESTION?
1. When are you going to
2. Where are you going to
3. Why are you going to
4. Who are you going to
5. What are you going to

WHAT'S MY LINE?
1. going
2. have, evening
3. is, weekend
4. are
5. now
6. are you going to
7. going to
8. am
9. once
10. going to get

SEGMENT 23

Page 106

YES OR NO?
1. Yes
2. No
3. Yes
4. Yes
5. Yes
6. No
7. Yes
8. Yes
9. Yes
10. Yes
11. No

A GOOD DAY FOR THE BEACH

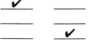

Page 107

WEATHER CHALLENGE!
1. cool
2. warm
3. hot
4. snow
5. clear
6. sunny
7. hot
8. warm
9. foggy
10. warm
11. hot
12. rain
13. drizzle
14. warm
15. sunny
16. hot
17. clear
18. cool
19. snow

Page 108

EDITING MIX-UP
4
3
1
6
5
2

SOUND CHECK
1. What
2. it
3. eleven
4. have
5. It's
6. fifteen
7. What's
8. time
9. thirty
10. Can
11. tell
12. forty-five
13. do
14. have
15. o'clock

Page 109

WHAT'S THE TIME?

1. 2:00
2. 3:30
3. 4:45
4. 5:15
5. 6:00
6. 7:45

Page 110

EDITING MIX-UP
4
2
5
7
1
6
8
3

WHOSE LINE?
1. Wife
2. Husband
3. Wife
4. Wife
5. Husband
6. Husband

Page 111

YES, NO, OR MAYBE?
1. Yes
2. No
3. Maybe
4. Yes
5. No
6. Yes
7. Yes
8. Yes
9. Yes
10. Yes
11. Yes
12. Maybe
13. No

Page 112

EDITING MIX-UP
3
6
5
1
4
2
7

Page 113

FINISH THE SONG!
1. week
2. year
3. wait
4. In
5. summer
6. fall
7. waiting
8. I'm
9. February
10. April
11. July
12. September
13. December
14. It's
15. after
16. past
17. to
18. wait
19. day
20. month
21. right
22. with
23. to be
24. you

WHAT'S NEXT?
1. March
2. July
3. evening
4. Wednesday
5. winter

Page 114

WHAT ARE THEY SAYING?
1. A. What, does
   B. leaves, half past three
2. A. is it
   B. a quarter to three
3. A. What time does
   B. begins, a quarter after eight
4. A. time
   B. twelve, midnight
5. A. Do
   B. It's a quarter to eight
6. A. What time, begin
   B. It, half past two

SEGMENT 24

Page 120

EDITING MIX-UP

a. 2 / 1 / 3

b. 3 / 2 / 1

c. 4 / 2 / 3 / 1

d. 4 / 2 / 1 / 3

e. 2 / 3 / 1

f. 2 / 4 / 1 / 3

PICTURE THIS!

1. c
2. f
3. b
4. e
5. a
6. d

Page 121

THE NEXT LINE

1. b
2. a
3. b
4. a
5. a
6. b

MATCH THE SENTENCES!

1. d
2. c
3. a
4. b

Page 122

PREVIEW

1. heachache
2. backache
3. stomachache
4. cold
5. sore throat
6. earache
7. toothache

SOUND CHECK

1. a
2. b
3. b
4. b
5. b
6. a
7. a

Page 123

SOUND CHECK

1. worked
2. cooked
3. washed
4. played
5. cleaned
6. studied
7. painted
8. planted
9. waited

Page 124

EDITING MIX-UP

2 / 4 / 1 / 6 / 7 / 3 / 5

Page 125

SOUND CHECK

1. stomachache
2. ate
3. headache
4. drank
5. backache
6. sat
7. throat
8. sang

THE NEXT LINE

1. a
2. b
3. a
4. a
5. b
6. a
7. a
8. a

Page 126

FINISH THE RAP!

1. washed
2. floors
3. floors
4. washed
5. floors
6. cleaned
7. house
8. house
9. cleaned
10. house
11. painted
12. porch
13. porch
14. painted
15. porch
16. fixed
17. sink
18. sink
19. fixed
20. sink
21. washed
22. cleaned
23. painted
24. fixed

Page 127

WHAT'S THE RIGHT WORD?

1. cleaned, backache
2. watches
3. ate, stomachache
4. played, played
5. waited
6. talked, listened
7. studied, studied
8. drink, headache
9. cooked, cleaned
10. exercise, exercised

WHAT DID THEY DO?

1. played
2. cleaned
3. ate
4. washed
5. cooked
6. sat
7. sang
8. drank

SEGMENT 25

Page 132

SOUND CHECK

1. Did
2. did
3. Did
4. brush
5. did
6. Did
7. sleep
8. didn't
9. Did you brush
10. didn't
11. brushed
12. your hair

Page 133

WHAT DID THEY DO?

1. worked in his garden
2. visited some old friends from college
3. talked, talked, talked
4. played baseball with her kids
5. stayed home and rested
6. prepared for Leonard's visit
7. dusted the furniture
8. vacuumed the rugs
9. cleaned all the bathrooms
10. washed the windows
11. cooked
12. baked

Page 134

YES, NO, OR MAYBE?

1. Yes
2. No
3. Maybe
4. No
5. Yes
6. Maybe
7. Maybe
8. Maybe

Page 135

WHERE DID THEY GO?

		✔
	✔	✔
✔	✔	✔

SOUND CHECK

1. Did
2. go
3. didn't
4. went
5. did
6. go
7. this
8. didn't
9. to the
10. go bowling
11. This
12. went
13. went
14. to the library
15. went
16. laundromat
17. go
18. went

Page 136

YES, NO, OR MAYBE?

1. Yes	12. Yes
2. No	13. Maybe
3. No	14. Yes
4. Maybe	15. Yes
5. No	16. Maybe
6. No	17. No
7. Maybe	18. Yes
8. Yes	19. Yes
9. Yes	20. No
10. Maybe	21. No
11. Yes	22. Yes

Page 137

SOUND CHECK

1. had	8. have
2. wrote	9. watched
3. read	10. rested
4. worked	11. took
5. left	12. read
6. missed	13. drank
7. had	14. went

WHAT'S MY LINE?

1. Did, take	took
2. Did, buy	bought
3. Did, get up	got up
4. Did, have	had
5. Did, write	wrote

Page 138

SOUND CHECK

1. bought	5. children
2. were	6. tired
3. was	7. we're
4. wife	8. bought

EDITING MIX-UP

3
5
7
8
2
9
1
10
11
4
6

Page 139

YES OR NO?

1. No	9. No
2. Yes	10. Yes
3. Yes	11. Yes
4. Yes	12. No
5. Yes	13. No
6. No	14. No
7. Yes	15. Yes
8. Yes	

EDITING MIX-UP 1

2
4
5
1
3

Page 140

EDITING MIX-UP 2

3
6
4
1
7
2
5

FIX THE COMMERCIALS!

1. Pet Food	5. Floor Wax
2. Toothpaste	6. Sofa
3. Shampoo	7. Vitamins
4. Paint	

Page 141

BAD WEATHER

1. He didn't go to the beach.
   He went to the movies.
2. She didn't work in the yard.
   She wrote letters.
3. She didn't wash the car.
   She studied English.
4. He didn't have a picnic.
   He ate at a restaurant.
5. She didn't walk to work.
   She took the bus.
6. He didn't paint the garage.
   He did his homework.
7. He didn't plant flowers.
   He read a novel.
8. She didn't play golf.
   She went bowling.

Page 142

TV CROSSWORD

See page 166.

SEGMENT 26

Page 148

WHERE WAS EVERYBODY?

1. was, movies
2. was, meeting
3. was, computer class
4. were, birthday party
5. were, ballgame

SOUND CHECK

1. wasn't	5. was
2. wasn't	6. was
3. weren't	7. were
4. wasn't	

THE NEXT LINE

1. b	4. a
2. b	5. b
3. b	6. b

Page 149

SOUND CHECK

1. Did	7. Did
2. did	8. did
3. was	9. were
4. Did	10. Did
5. didn't	11. didn't
6. wasn't	12. weren't

Pages 150–151

ON CAMERA

1. were	17. was
2. was	18. weren't
3. were	19. were
4. was	20. was
5. was	21. were
6. were	22. were
7. was	23. was
8. were	24. was
9. were	25. went
10. wasn't	26. didn't
11. were	27. went
12. were	28. didn't
13. were	29. go
14. wasn't	30. went
15. was	31. went
16. were	32. sat

33. talked
34. didn't
35. go
36. didn't
37. sit
38. went
39. looked
40. was
41. was
42. was
43. went
44. did
45. sat
46. talked
47. ate
48. had

49. did
50. was
51. started
52. rain
53. didn't
54. rain
55. was
56. wasn't
57. wasn't
58. rained
59. didn't
60. rain
61. did
62. was
63. was
64. was

Page 152

WHAT'S THE RESPONSE?

1. j
2. f
3. h
4. g
5. d
6. c
7. i
8. b
9. a
10. e

WHAT'S THE WORD?

1. was
2. Did
3. weren't
4. were
5. was, didn't, wasn't
6. weren't
7. didn't, was
8. was, wasn't
9. didn't, was
10. were, weren't, didn't, were, Were, was

Page 153

MATCH THE LINES!

1. f
2. d
3. h
4. g
5. a
6. e
7. c
8. b

SCRAMBLED SOUND TRACK

1. Tommy's father was at a meeting.
2. Were you at your computer class?
3. It didn't rain. It was sunny./ It was sunny. It didn't rain.
4. Tommy's grandparents were at the ballgame.
5. We had a big dinner because we were hungry.
6. They went to the zoo and looked at the animals.
7. I didn't go to work yesterday because I was very sick.
8. We didn't eat ice cream. We ate popcorn./We didn't eat popcorn. We ate ice cream.
9. They sat on a bench in the park, and they talked for hours and hours.

Page 44

TV CROSSWORD

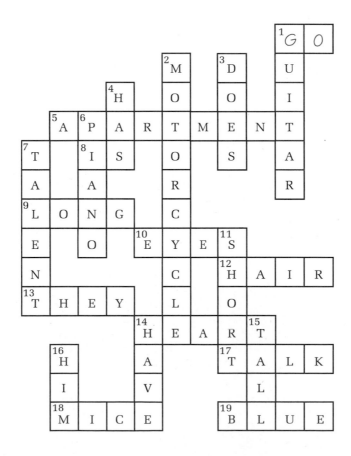

TV CROSSWORD

```
 T  E  E  T  H        T  O  O  K              V  I  T  A  M  I  N  S
 O        H           O                       I
          E           O           P     W  A  S
 C  O  M  F  O  R  T  A  B  L  E     R        I
 L              H              T  O  O     T  H  I  S
 E        S  H  A  M  P  O  O     S        E        A
 A        A        A              T     D  U  S  T  E  D     D
 N        D  O     S           S  A  D                       I
 E        A        T           O                             D
 D           B  R  E  A  K  F  A  S  T
             U        T        A
             Y        E
```